CW00530979

Diagnostic SpellingTests

Diagnostic Spelling Tests 3–5

secondary/adult

spelling assessment and diagnostic follow-up for ages 11 to adult

Mary Crumpler and Colin McCarty

HODDER
EDUCATION
AN HACHETTE UK COMPANY

Acknowledgements

We thank Margaret Lorman-Hall and her team for marking all the answer booklets from the standardisation trials and entering the data. This ensured the highest quality of marking and reliability for the independent statistical tests and reports prepared by Tony Kiek.

We also are much indebted to Marie Lallaway and Mike de la Mare for authoring some of the detailed commentaries on each of the spelling tests, providing valuable and useful information to assist teachers and others who use these tests to help students learn to become better at spelling the words that make up our language.

We are profoundly grateful to our publisher, Charles Knight, for his close involvement and encouragement throughout all stages of this project and his many helpful suggestions and advice.

We wish to record our thanks to the staff and students in the following schools, training organisations and services, who took part in the initial and final standardisation trials for *Diagnostic Spelling Tests 3–5*:

All Saints Primary School, Coventry
Allesley Primary School, Coventry
Aylesbury Training Group, Aylesbury
BETA, Basingstoke
Brenda Soar Training, Newmarket
Brinsworth Training Ltd, Rotherham
Chesham High School, Chesham
Coventry Learning Support Service
Dr Challoner's Grammar School, High Wycombe
Grange Farm Primary School, Coventry
Haresfoot Preparatory School, Cheshunt
HETA, Humberside
Hyde Park Junior School, Plymouth
John Gulson Primary School, Coventry
Kingham Hill School, Kingham Hill
Leamington Centre, Warwickshire College
Leeds Grammar School, Leeds

Limbrick Wood Primary School, Coventry
Little Heath School, Reading
Mountfitchet High School, Stansted
NLT Training Services Ltd, Chesterfield
Sarah Craig, Dyslexia Tutor, Folkestone
SETA, Stockport
SETA, Washington
St Bernadette's Primary School, Wallsend
Swanbourne House School, Milton Keynes
Temple Sutton Primary School, Southend
The Hurst Community College, Tadley
Twynham School, Christchurch
Westborough Primary School, Southend
Westbourne House School, Chichester
Whitely Abbey Primary School, Coventry
Windsor and Maidenhead Learning Support Service

Orders: please contact Hachette UK Distribution, Hely Hutchinson Centre, Milton Road, Didcot, Oxfordshire, OX11 7HH. Telephone: 01235 400555. Lines are open from 9 a.m. to 5 p.m., Monday to Friday, with a 24-hour message answering service. Email: primary@hachette.co.uk. You can also order through our website www.hoddereducation.co.uk.

British Library Cataloguing in Publication Data
A catalogue record for this title is available from the British Library

ISBN-13 978 0 340 91280 5

First published 2006
Impression number 14
Year   2021

Copyright © 2006 Hodder and Stoughton Ltd

All rights reserved. This work is copyright. Permission is given for copies to be made of pages identified as photocopiable resources, provided they are used exclusively within the institution for which this work has been purchased. For reproduction for any other purpose, permission must first be obtained in writing from the publishers.

Typeset by Phoenix Photosetting, Chatham, Kent
Printed in Great Britain for Hodder Education, an Hachette UK Company, Carmelite House, 50 Victoria Embankment, London EC4Y 0DZ by Hobbs the Printers Ltd, Totton, Hampshire SO40 3WX

Contents

Test 3

Test 4

Test 5

Introduction

The *Diagnostic Spelling Tests* are a series of five easy-to-administer group or individual spelling tests for students throughout their school years and beyond. Each test is designed to be administered to whole classes or large groups, but may be used with individuals or small groups if preferred. Each test is provided in two parallel forms (Form A and Form B), which are carefully matched in content, style and difficulty, and which enable you to measure progress over time or after specific intervention.

The complete set of tests are is listed below. *Diagnostic Spelling Tests 3–5* are for students from secondary school age up to adulthood (*Diagnostic Spelling Test 3* also forms part of the Primary materials):

Diagnostic Spelling Test 1	ages 5–7	Years 1 and 2
Diagnostic Spelling Test 2	ages 7–9	Years 3 and 4
Diagnostic Spelling Test 3	ages 9–12	Years 5, 6 and 7
Diagnostic Spelling Test 4	ages 11–15	Years 7, 8, 9 and 10
Diagnostic Spelling Test 5	ages 15–20+	Year 10 up to adult

Diagnostic Spelling Test 3 is based on the National Literacy Strategy objectives for Years 5 and 6, so is ideal for assessing students' spelling in Year 7 when they enter secondary education and start Key Stage 3. This test requires the use of printed test forms A and/or B, available separately. Photocopiable analysis grids, together with diagnostic information and supplementary materials, are provided on pages 15–22.

Diagnostic Spelling Test 4 is based on the KS3 National Strategy *Framework for Teaching English: Years 7, 8 and 9* (DfEE, 2001), including frequently used, but often incorrectly spelt, technical words associated with all curriculum subjects. *Diagnostic Spelling Test 5* is designed to test spelling associated with functional literacy, and includes words identified by YELL to be commonly mis-spelled on website enquiries, and words that journalists identified as being difficult to spell.

Purposes and uses of the tests

The *Diagnostic Spelling Tests* provide a standardised assessment of a student's spelling ability and the opportunity to analyse the spelling patterns that he or she is able to use effectively and those which may need further teaching and practice.

Following an intervention programme, progress can be assessed globally, by re-testing with the alternate Form, or specifically, by using the follow-up tests provided in this book. Each follow-up test focuses on one type of spelling structure – e.g. double consonants, word endings and suffixes – which can be diagnosed using the marking sheets and overlays provided as photocopy masters.

Interpreting the diagnostic information

Examining how students spell the words in any of the *Diagnostic Spelling Tests* can give useful diagnostic information on their learning of English spelling. It may indicate:

- whether or not particular aspects of spelling have been learned;
- how effectively spelling rules may have been understood;
- whether individual students and/or groups of students are finding specific aspects of spelling especially difficult.

Teachers may then wish to revisit particular spelling patterns with their classes, offer their students a range of strategies for learning spellings, or consider particular programmes or approaches for students struggling with spelling.

Diagnostic information can be gained through looking at:

- which kinds of words are being misspelled and which kinds are spelled correctly;
- what sorts of errors are being made in the misspelled words.

To assist with the first of these, there is a marking grid and set of marking-overlay masters for each test showing which words in the specific *Diagnostic Spelling Tests* illustrate particular spelling patterns or need to be learned as 'sight words'.[1]

Early spelling development

Initially many young children will show they understand that marks on paper can stand for spoken words by making random scribbles or letter-like marks that bear no relation to the actual spelling of the words or the sounds within them. A point comes, however, when a connection is made between the sound of a word and the letters used to represent it. The first phoneme in a word is likely to be prominent in this process, followed later by the final phoneme, especially where this is a consonant. Early on, letter names are sometimes used to represent sequences of sounds, so that *elephant* may be spelled as *lfet*, or the name *Jean* as *gn*, a process sometimes referred to as 'invented spelling'. Proficiency in phonics is likely to develop to the point where many simple words are spelled either accurately or in a phonologically plausible way. However, this 'alphabetic phase' is not sufficient for accurate spelling in English, where knowledge of the actual sequence of letters in specific words is needed if they are to be spelled accurately. When a child remembers automatically the spelling of many English words – that is, has a large repertoire of 'sight words' – he or she can be considered to have reached an 'orthographic phase'.[2]

---

[1] The expression 'sight word' is commonly used to refer to a word where the sequence of letters is remembered automatically and can be spelled without recourse to conscious phonics. It relates to recognising words immediately on sight when reading. It does not imply that a visual strategy has been used to learn such words.

[2] The theory of developmental phases presented here is based on Frith, U. (1985) 'Beneath the surface of developmental dyslexia', in Patterson, K. E., Marshall, J. C. and Coltheart, M. (eds), *Surface Dyslexia: Neuropsychological and Cognitive Studies of Phonological Reading*, Lawrence Erlbaum.

These phases should not be thought of as a discrete series of steps, however, but rather as the main focus of how a child spells. During the alphabetic phase, some words (such as the child's own name) will be known without resorting to phonics, while, at the orthographic phase, alphabetic/phonic strategies will still be available for unfamiliar words. How early literacy is taught will also have an impact – for instance, if letter names are not used to start with, then a child is less likely to use them to 'invent' spellings; if phonics is taught intensively at a young age, the alphabetic phase will be embarked on earlier than it might otherwise be.

It can be seen that children may experience difficulty at either the alphabetic phase or the orthographic phase or both. At the alphabetic phase, a difficulty identifying the sounds in words (segmenting words into their constituent phonemes) will limit progress in phonics, as will a difficulty remembering which letters or groups of letters are associated with which phonemes. On the other hand, some children may become adept at phonics, but still find it very hard to remember the actual sequence of letters in specific words (to develop a sight vocabulary). These weaknesses could continue with the child all the way to adulthood, but finding out strengths and weaknesses will enable strategies to be implemented to help overcome difficulties.

Diagnostic Spelling Test 3

Both Form A and Form B of Test 3 comprise three cloze passages; Passage A has twelve items and Passages B and C have fourteen items each.

The 40 items were selected to cover objectives from the National Literacy Strategy for the third term of Year 4, all six terms of Years 5 and 6 and the first term of Year 7, as shown below. This broad spread makes the test ideal for quick screening on entry to secondary school, and for more detailed diagnostic follow-up when appropriate.

Year 4	<ul><li>Words with common letter strings but different pronunciations, e.g. *tough, through, trough, plough*</li><li>Words with common suffixes, e.g. *-ible, -able, -ive, -sion, -tion*</li><li>*It's/its*</li><li>Medium-frequency words</li></ul>
Year 5	<ul><li>Words with common prefixes, e.g. *auto-, bi-, trans-, tele-, circum-*</li><li>Medium-frequency words</li><li>Words with soft 'c', e.g. *ceiling*</li><li>Homophones</li><li>Words with common suffixes, e.g. *-cian, -ssion, -ation, -etion, -ition, -otion, -ution*</li><li>Polysyllabic words with unstressed vowels, e.g. *literacy*</li><li>Words ending in modifying 'e' drop 'e' when adding 'ing' but not when adding suffix beginning with a consonant, e.g. *hoping/hopeful*</li><li>'i' before 'e' except after 'c' when the sound is 'ee', e.g. *receive*</li></ul>
Year 6	Word roots, prefixes and suffixes
Year 7	Apostrophes denoting possession

The tables on page 14 give all of the 40 words in Form A and Form B and shows the diagnostic categories into which they may be classified.

Giving the test

The test is designed to enable it to be administered to whole classes or large groups, but it may be used with individuals or small groups if this is preferred. The tests are provided in two parallel forms to measure progress over time or after specific intervention.

Timing

No time limit is set, but the test is likely to take between 20 and 30 minutes for most classes. The test is paced by the person administering it, as the items are read aloud to the students. It is suggested that about 15 seconds are allowed for the students to write the answer.

Procedure

Each student will need a copy of the test booklet and writing materials. Answers may be altered by rubbing or crossing out. It is important that the students work alone, without copying or discussing their answers. Generally students will record their own answers in the test booklet but may, if necessary, dictate them letter-by-letter to an adult.

Give each student a copy of the test booklet. Introduce the test by telling the students that you are giving them a spelling test, and they should do their best to spell correctly all the words you are going to ask them to write. Tell them that there will be some words that they can spell easily, but that there are also some harder words. They should not worry if they find some difficult, but just try their best. Remind them to write as neatly and legibly as possible.

Before starting the test, ask the students to complete the details on the front page. Suggested wording for administering the test is given below, but this may be adapted – the most important thing is that the students understand what they have to do.

Administering Diagnostic Spelling Test 3: Form A

First, read the general instructions for administering the test, above. Then use the guide wording below to present the test. (Note: capitalisation is ignored in the scoring.)

Open the booklet and look at the first page. There is a passage with some of the words missing. There is a line to show you where a word is missing.

I'm going to read the whole passage to you first, and I want you to listen to it carefully. Then I will read it again, and when I get to the words that are missing, I will stop and give you time to write them on the lines. Listen first. Follow the words as I read.

I enjoy going **swimming** with my **brother** and **sister**, **except** when we have to go **inside** the **draughty** changing rooms. I **know** it's going to be like that, but I still shiver: it's **automatic**.

I'm **relieved** when I get into the warm pool. Then I really enjoy the training **session**. I only feel **miserable** if I get water in my **eyes**.

Now I'll read it again, and this time you are going to write in the missing words.

I enjoy going **swimming** [pause] with my **brother** [pause] and **sister** [pause], **except** [pause] when we have to go **inside** [pause] the **draughty** [pause] changing rooms. I **know** [pause] it's going to be like that, but I still shiver: it's **automatic** [pause].

I'm **relieved** [pause] when I get into the warm pool. Then I really enjoy the training **session** [pause]. I only feel **miserable** [pause] if I get water in my **eyes** [pause].

Look at the next page. We're going to do exactly the same thing with this passage. Listen carefully and follow the words as I read.

The **freight** train pulled out of the **station** in the **direction** of London. As the driver travelled the **familiar route**, he began to enjoy the journey **between** the two cities through the **different** landscapes.

Ahead, a train came into **view**. It should have been **stationary**, but it seemed to be travelling at **excessive** speed. He **applied** the **brake** and hoped it would **work**. If the two trains were on the same track, there would be a **collision**.

Now I'll read it again, and this time you are going to write in the missing words.

The **freight** [pause] train pulled out of the **station** [pause] in the **direction** [pause] of London. As the driver travelled the **familiar** [pause] **route** [pause], he began to enjoy the journey **between** [pause] the two cities through the **different** [pause] landscapes.

Ahead, a train came into **view** [pause]. It should have been **stationary** [pause], but it seemed to be travelling at **excessive** [pause] speed. He **applied** [pause] the **brake** [pause] and hoped it would **work** [pause]. If the two trains were on the same track, there would be a **collision** [pause].

Turn over and listen to the last passage. Follow the words as I read.

Yesterday the government introduced a **White Paper** on looking after the **earth** and its resources – an **important** issue for the **whole world**.

The **minister previewed** a **memorable** speech to an enthusiastic **audience**. She said, 'The government's **primary** aim is **shaming** those countries that are **careless** with their natural resources.'

Would the **superpowers** be impressed?

Now I'll read it again, and this time you are going to write in the missing words.

Yesterday the government introduced a **White** [pause] **Paper** [pause] on looking after the **earth** [pause] and its resources – an **important** [pause] issue for the **whole** [pause] **world** [pause].

The **minister** [pause] **previewed** [pause] a **memorable** [pause] speech to an enthusiastic **audience** [pause]. She said, 'The government's **primary** [pause] aim is **shaming** [pause] those countries that are **careless** [pause] with their natural resources.'

Would the **superpowers** [pause] be impressed?

OK, that's the end of the test. Put your pencils/pens down now.

Test 3

First, read the general instructions for administering the test, on page 5. Then use the guide wording below to present the test.

Open the booklet and look at the first page. There is a passage with some of the words missing. There is a line to show you where a word is missing.

I'm going to read the whole passage to you first, and I want you to listen to it carefully. Then I will read it again, and when I get to the words that are missing, I will stop and give you time to write them on the lines. Listen first. Follow the words as I read.

The **children** were lounging about in the **centre** of the **garden**. They could **hear** their **mother's** angry **discussion** on the **telephone**. They **thought** she was talking to their **father** but did not know for certain.

They were **uncomfortable** that their **neighbour** might be **listening** to the argument.

Now I'll read it again, and this time you are going to write in the missing words.

The **children** [pause] were lounging about in the **centre** [pause] of the **garden** [pause]. They could **hear** [pause] their **mother's** [pause] angry **discussion** [pause] on the **telephone** [pause]. They **thought** [pause] she was talking to their **father** [pause] but did not know for certain.

They were **uncomfortable** [pause] that their **neighbour** [pause] might be **listening** [pause] to the argument.

Look at the next page. We're going to do exactly the same thing with this passage. Listen carefully and follow the words as I read.

Our **situation** was **awful** and I was **desperate** to get away. How could I **prevent** something **terrible** happening? I tried to think of a **solution** but I was not **hopeful**.

We heard a **cough**. It was a **frightening sound**. We **both** jumped. I wanted to **steal** away, but I did not want to appear **weak** in front of my **friend**.

Now I'll read it again, and this time you are going to write in the missing words.

Our **situation** [pause] was **awful** [pause] and I was **desperate** [pause] to get away. How could I **prevent** [pause] something **terrible** [pause] happening? I tried to think of a **solution** [pause] but I was not **hopeful** [pause].

We heard a **cough** [pause]. It was a **frightening** [pause] **sound** [pause]. We **both** [pause] jumped. I wanted to **steal** [pause] away, but I did not want to appear **weak** [pause] in front of my **friend** [pause].

Turn over and listen to the last passage. Follow the words as I read.

Some people **definitely** enjoy buying **clothes** and yet there are **those** who hate it. My sister spends an **incredible** amount of time looking in shop **windows** even if she has no **money**.

When we go **round** town **together**, she calls **either** Jasmine or Kerry and sends them **photographs** of the latest **fashions**. It's my **brother's** mobile, so I make her **include** me in the **pictures** too.

Now I'll read it again, and this time you are going to write in the missing words.

Some people **definitely** [pause] enjoy buying **clothes** [pause] and yet there are **those** [pause] who hate it. My sister spends an **incredible** [pause] amount of time looking in shop **windows** [pause] even if she has no **money** [pause].

When we go **round** [pause] town **together** [pause], she calls **either** [pause] Jasmine or Kerry and sends them **photographs** [pause] of the latest **fashions** [pause]. It's my **brother's** [pause] mobile, so I make her **include** [pause] me in the **pictures** [pause] too.

OK, that's the end of the test. Put your pencils/pens down now.

Marking

Once the student has completed the spelling test, their answers may be marked and, if required, analysed. Mark each spelling as correct or incorrect, awarding one mark for each correct answer. If a student has made more than one attempt to spell a word, only mark the one that he or she has indicated is the final answer. If a word is illegible, check with the student if possible; otherwise, mark the word as incorrect.

- Scoring by students is not recommended, for even if papers are switched around to obviate any alterations, the scoring tends to be very inaccurate.
- Each correct word counts 1; no half-marks are allowed for 'nearly correct' or 'doubtful' answers.
- Omissions, like wrong spellings, count as zero.
- The correct part of speech is essential. For example, *picture* is not accepted for *pictures*; also *picture's* is wrong.
- Ignore all capitalisations, regardless of whether they should be either present or absent (because of the sentence structure or if the word is a proper noun).
- Inserted hyphens (e.g. *super-powers*) are wrong.
- If there is doubt about certain letters, they can usually be identified by comparing with the same letters in other words or you may check with the student if appropriate. Insertions are accepted if in the right place, but letter reversals are not.

To assist marking, page total scores should be recorded at the bottom right of each page of the test booklets. These subtotals should be transferred to the summary box on the front cover of the test and the total raw score worked out. The student's chronological age on taking the test should be recorded in years and completed months. The standardised scores, percentiles and spelling age may then be found from the conversion tables on pages 75–7. Where students have not done well, their answers can be analysed to find if there are specific patterns of weakness.

Using the diagnostic analysis sheets

Once the tests have all been marked, you may wish to analyse some students' results in more detail, examining their answers for relative strengths and areas that require further teaching and reinforcement activities. Photocopy masters of marking and analysis sheets for *Diagnostic Spelling Test 3* are provided on pages 15–22.

First, transfer the information from the student's test paper onto a photocopy of the marking grid for the correct Form (see pages 15 and 19). We suggest that in the boxes to the right of the words you show correct answers by a ✓, incorrect ones with an ✗ and leave blank questions that were not attempted.

Next, make up a set of diagnostic overlays by photocopying the masters in this manual onto thermal OHP transparencies. *Note:* use only the correct thermal film, as ordinary OHP sheets will ruin the photocopier.

Inspecting the marking grid through the different analysis overlays should enable you to determine any patterns of strengths and areas for further work. A more detailed investigation of a student's actual answers may then be worthwhile, once you have established any overarching patterns using the overlays.

Once you have determined the areas which need addressing, you can utilise a variety of strategies to help your students improve. Useful guidance is provided in the *Diagnostic Analysis* section, below.

Checking progress

To help you to check on a student's further progress, there is a suite of short, focused 'diagnostic checks' to use as follow-up tests for each of the categories. Photocopiable answer sheets for students, and a page giving the target words and script for the teacher, teaching assistant or learning support assistant to read from, are given on pages 23–6 to enable you to deliver these focused tests.

At a later stage, you may then wish to use the parallel form of the test to assess overall progress.

Prefixes

Prefixes are added at the beginnings of words to change their meanings (*incredible, previewed, superpowers*). The same prefixes tend to occur in many different words, and so learning a relatively small number of them can make the spelling of a large number of words more accurate, including longer words and words not encountered before.

Discussing the meaning and origins of prefixes with students can be interesting and can help them retain their spelling. Examples from *Diagnostic Spelling Test 3* include the *tele-* in *telephone*, which comes from an Ancient Greek word meaning 'far off'. The same prefix can be seen in *television* and *telescope*. The *super-* in *superpowers* is a Latin word meaning 'above', and can be seen also in *supermarket* and *Superman*.

Suffixes/common word endings

Suffixes are added to the ends of words to change their meaning or their grammatical function (*swimming, uncomfortable, hopeful, definitely*). As with prefixes, learning a relatively small number of them can make the spelling of a large number of words more accurate, including longer words and words not encountered before. The same is true of learning some other common word endings (*session, together*) that are not strictly speaking suffixes.

Diagnostic Spelling Test 3 includes many words with suffixes and other common word endings, allowing a detailed examination of which of them students have become familiar with. It is particularly valuable to look for words where the word as a whole is misspelled, but the suffix is spelled accurately, suggesting the student is making good use of morphemic strategies.

Words with double consonants

One aspect of spelling that even quite advanced spellers find difficult is remembering whether specific words contain single or double consonants. *Diagnostic Spelling Test 3* includes a number of words containing double consonants. These words fall roughly into the following categories:

- those where there is a double consonant as the result of a suffixing rule (*swimming*);
- those where there are historical reasons relating to prefixes (*applied, collision, different*);
- those where a double *s* indicates that *s* before *ion* is pronounced /sh/ not /zh/ (*session, discussion*);
- those where the double consonant indicates the preceding vowel is a short vowel (*excessive, terrible*), and the preceding syllable is stressed (the *te-* of *terrible* is pronounced more heavily than the *-rrible*).

Where the first of these is still proving difficult, further attention to suffixing rules may be needed. Where the others are resulting in misspellings, exploration of regularities may be worthwhile. In the end, however, students are likely to need to remember which specific words contain double letters. The sight-word strategies suggested below (under *'Irregular' words*) can be used, but with particular emphasis on the doubled letters – for instance, in a visual strategy, the letters can be written in a different colour.

Homophones

Homophones are words that sound the same but are spelled differently. Those in *Diagnostic Spelling Test 3* are: *except* (accept), *know* (no), *route* (root), *brake* (break), *whole* (hole), *world* (whirled), *hear* (here), *mother's* (mothers), *steal* (steel), *weak* (week), *brother's* (brothers).

Where students provide the wrong spelling, it may indicate a number of things:

■ They may not be familiar with the actual spelling and so are using their phonics to attempt the word (*hole* is phonologically more plausible than the actual spelling of *whole*: the fact that *hole* is a real word would be coincidental).
■ They may not be familiar with the actual spelling and so are relying on a known spelling of a word pronounced the same as the target word (the spelling of *root* may be already known, but not *route*).
■ They may be familiar with both words, but select the wrong one.

In the first two instances, a memory for the actual spellings of words needs to be developed (see below, under *'Irregular' words*).

The final instance suggests the link between meaning and spelling is not sufficiently strong. It is important that words should be written, and read, in a meaningful context as much as possible, and it may also be useful to look explicitly at pairs of words, exploring the meanings of each.

Medium-frequency words

These are words selected from those specified in the NLS as requiring a particular spelling focus in Year 4 and Year 5. As well as being relatively common, many of them are easily confused or do not follow a regular pattern. The intention is therefore that they should be learned as 'sight words', where the exact sequence of letters is remembered, allowing the words to be spelled quickly and automatically. Students can then use them in their own writing without, for instance, having to make conscious use of phonics, and so allowing more attention to be given to the content of their writing.

Where a significant number of these words are misspelled on the test, it could indicate that insufficient attention has been given to the learning of them or that students are not being given sufficient opportunity to write (and so to use the words repeatedly in a meaningful context).

'Irregular' words

These are words that it would be difficult to spell accurately through the straightforward application of phonic rules. However, it is important to remember that what counts as regular and what counts as irregular depends on the phonic patterns and rules that have already been taught and the frequency of their occurrence.

For *Diagnostic Spelling Test 3* we have provided a separate category of sight words in the diagnostic overlays, as this information may well be more helpful to teachers trying to determine where a student may be experiencing difficulties than examining their performance on words that are categorised by the NLS as high- or medium-frequency words.

Where the actual sequence of letters has not been learned, but a student's basic phonics is good, misspellings are likely to be plausible – for instance *draughty* spelled as *drarfty*, *freight* as *frate* or *frait*, or *listening* as *lisning*. This may suggest that although the alphabetic phase has been mastered in spelling, moving through the orthographic phase to acquire a large spelling vocabulary is proving problematic.

Teaching students how to learn sight words is often overlooked. Possible strategies include:

- *Visualisation* – the student looks at the word written in large letters, and then tries to see it inside their head, perhaps changing the colours of the letters or saying what letters they can see.
- *Auditory strategies* – using spelling pronunciations (pronouncing the *er* in *desperate* and making the *ate* rhyme with *eight*, or pronouncing the *ten* in *listening*), or taping themselves saying aloud the sequence of letters in a word and then playing it back a number of times.
- *Kinaesthetic strategies* – remembering the movement the hand makes when writing a word, by, for instance, using a finger to trace a number of times over a word written in large letters, then repeating the movement with a pencil.
- *Mnemonics* – memory tricks usually using memorable sentences or phrases (<u>b</u>ig <u>e</u>lephants <u>c</u>an <u>a</u>ll <u>u</u>nderstand <u>s</u>mall <u>e</u>lephants = *because*), ideally made up by the students themselves.

Research suggests that it is beneficial to help students select their own best strategy for learning the spelling of 'sight words'.[3]

Next steps

Once the students' test results have been analysed using the diagnostic overlays, patterns of errors may well have been revealed and areas identified that require further teaching and reinforcement activities – for example, prefixes or suffixes.

Whichever strategy, or combination of strategies, is used, it is important that students develop a habit of checking spelling attempts when they are practising a word – otherwise they will often be reinforcing a misspelling of a word. Encouraging them to check each letter aloud in turn with a model written by an adult can be helpful.

After a period of additional work, you may wish to check the students' progress on the specific area covered: short, focused tests are provided for this purpose on pages 23–6, covering medium-frequency words, homophones, double consonants, prefixes and suffixes/common word endings.

[3] Brooks, P. and Weekes, S. (1999) *Individual Styles in Learning to Spell: Improving Spelling in Children with Literacy Difficulties and all Children in Mainstream Schools*, DfEE Publications.

DST 3 Form A

DST 3 Form A	Medium-frequency words (Y4/5)	Homophones	Words with double consonant	Prefixes	Suffixes/ Common word ends	Sight words
swimming	✓				✓	
brother	✓		✓		✓	✓
sister	✓				✓	
except		✓		✓		✓
inside	✓			✓	✓	✓
draughty					✓	✓
know		✓				✓
automatic				✓		✓
relieved				✓	✓	✓
session			✓	✓	✓	
miserable					✓	✓
eyes	✓				✓	✓
freight						
station						✓
direction					✓	✓
familiar					✓	
route		✓				
between	✓			✓	✓	✓
different	✓		✓	✓	✓	
view		✓				✓
stationary				✓	✓	✓
excessive			✓	✓	✓	
applied			✓	✓	✓	
brake		✓				✓
work	✓				✓	
collision	✓		✓		✓	✓
White	✓					
Paper	✓				✓	✓
earth	✓					
important	✓			✓	✓	✓
whole	✓	✓				✓
world	✓	✓				✓
minister					✓	✓
previewed				✓	✓	
memorable					✓	✓
audience				✓	✓	
primary					✓	
shaming					✓	
careless					✓	
superpowers				✓	✓	

DST 3 Form B

DST 3 Form B	Medium-frequency words (Y4/5)	Homophones	Words with double consonant	Prefixes	Suffixes/ Common word ends	Sight words
children	✓				✓	
centre						✓
garden	✓					
hear		✓			✓	✓
mothers	✓	✓				
discussion			✓	✓	✓	
telephone				✓	✓	
thought	✓				✓	✓
father	✓				✓	
uncomfortable				✓	✓	
neighbour					✓	✓
listening					✓	✓
situation					✓	
awful					✓	
desperate				✓	✓	✓
prevent				✓	✓	
terrible			✓		✓	
solution					✓	
hopeful					✓	
cough						✓
frightening					✓	✓
sound	✓				✓	
both	✓				✓	
steal		✓				
weak		✓				
friend	✓					
definitely				✓	✓	✓
clothes	✓					✓
those	✓				✓	
incredible				✓	✓	
windows	✓				✓	
money	✓					
round	✓					
together	✓			✓	✓	✓
either					✓	
photographs				✓	✓	
fashions					✓	✓
brother's	✓	✓			✓	✓
include				✓	✓	
pictures					✓	✓

DST 3, Form A: Analysis for

	swimming		miserable		stationary		whole
	brother		eyes		excessive		world
	sister		freight		applied		minister
	except		station		brake		previewed
	inside		direction		work		memorable
	draughty		familiar		collision		audience
	know		route		White		primary
	automatic		between		Paper		shaming
	relieved		different		earth		careless
	session		view		important		super-powers

In the boxes to the right of the words, show correct by ✓, incorrect by ✗, and leave blank unattempted questions.

Diagnostic Spelling Tests photocopy master published by Hodder Murray

---

DST 3, Form A: Analysis for

	swimming		miserable		stationary		whole
	brother		eyes		excessive		world
	sister		freight		applied		minister
	except		station		brake		previewed
	inside		direction		work		memorable
	draughty		familiar		collision		audience
	know		route		White		primary
	automatic		between		Paper		shaming
	relieved		different		earth		careless
	session		view		important		super-powers

In the boxes to the right of the words, show correct by ✓, incorrect by ✗, and leave blank unattempted questions.

Diagnostic Spelling Tests photocopy master published by Hodder Murray

DST 3, Form A: medium-frequency words

swimming	miserable	stationary	whole
brother	eyes	excessive	world
sister	freight	applied	minister
except	station	brake	previewed
inside	direction	work	memorable
draughty	familiar	collision	audience
know	route	White	primary
automatic	between	Paper	shaming
relieved	different	earth	careless
session	view	important	super-powers

DST 3, Form A: homophones

swimming	miserable	stationary	whole
brother	eyes	excessive	world
sister	freight	applied	minister
except	station	brake	previewed
inside	direction	work	memorable
draughty	familiar	collision	audience
know	route	White	primary
automatic	between	Paper	shaming
relieved	different	earth	careless
session	view	important	super-powers

DST 3, Form A: double consonants

swimming   miserable   stationary   whole
brother   eyes   excessive   world
sister   freight   applied   minister
except   station   brake   previewed
inside   direction   work   memorable
draughty   familiar   collision   audience
know   route   White   primary
automatic   between   Paper   shaming
relieved   different   earth   careless
session   view   important   super-powers

DST 3, Form A: prefixes

swimming   miserable   stationary   whole
brother   eyes   excessive   world
sister   freight   applied   minister
except   station   brake   previewed
inside   direction   work   memorable
draughty   familiar   collision   audience
know   route   White   primary
automatic   between   Paper   shaming
relieved   different   earth   careless
session   view   important   super-powers

DST 3, Form A: word endings/suffixes

swimming   miserable   stationary   whole

brother   eyes   excessive   world

sister   freight   applied   minister

except   station   brake   previewed

inside   direction   work   memorable

draughty   familiar   collision   audience

know   route   White   primary

automatic   between   Paper   shaming

relieved   different   earth   careless

session   view   important   super-powers

DST 3, Form A: sight words

swimming   miserable   stationary   whole

brother   eyes   excessive   world

sister   freight   applied   minister

except   station   brake   previewed

inside   direction   work   memorable

draughty   familiar   collision   audience

know   route   White   primary

automatic   between   Paper   shaming

relieved   different   earth   careless

session   view   important   super-powers

DST 3, Form B: Analysis for

children		neighbour		frightening		windows	
centre		listening		sound		money	
garden		situation		both		round	
hear		awful		steal		together	
mother's		desperate		weak		either	
discussion		prevent		friend		photo-graphs	
telephone		terrible		definitely		fashions	
thought		solution		clothes		brother's	
father		hopeful		those		include	
uncomfort-able		cough		incredible		pictures	

In the boxes to the right of the words, show correct by ✓, incorrect by ✗, and leave blank unattempted questions.

Diagnostic Spelling Tests photocopy master published by Hodder Murray

---

DST 3, Form B: Analysis for

children		neighbour		frightening		windows	
centre		listening		sound		money	
garden		situation		both		round	
hear		awful		steal		together	
mother's		desperate		weak		either	
discussion		prevent		friend		photo-graphs	
telephone		terrible		definitely		fashions	
thought		solution		clothes		brother's	
father		hopeful		those		include	
uncomfort-able		cough		incredible		pictures	

In the boxes to the right of the words, show correct by ✓, incorrect by ✗, and leave blank unattempted questions.

Diagnostic Spelling Tests photocopy master published by Hodder Murray

DST 3, Form B: medium-frequency words

children	neighbour	frightening	windows
centre	listening	sound	money
garden	situation	both	round
hear	awful	steal	together
mother's	desperate	weak	either
discussion	prevent	friend	photo-graphs
telephone	terrible	definitely	fashions
thought	solution	clothes	brother's
father	hopeful	those	include
uncomfort-able	cough	incredible	pictures

DST 3, Form B: homophones

children	neighbour	frightening	windows
centre	listening	sound	money
garden	situation	both	round
hear	awful	steal	together
mother's	desperate	weak	either
discussion	prevent	friend	photo-graphs
telephone	terrible	definitely	fashions
thought	solution	clothes	brother's
father	hopeful	those	include
uncomfort-able	cough	incredible	pictures

DST 3, Form B: double consonants

children	neighbour	frightening	windows
centre	listening	sound	money
garden	situation	both	round
hear	awful	steal	together
mother's	desperate	weak	either
discussion	prevent	friend	photographs
telephone	terrible	definitely	fashions
thought	solution	clothes	brother's
father	hopeful	those	include
uncomfortable	cough	incredible	pictures

DST 3, Form B: prefixes

children	neighbour	frightening	windows
centre	listening	sound	money
garden	situation	both	round
hear	awful	steal	together
mother's	desperate	weak	either
discussion	prevent	friend	photographs
telephone	terrible	definitely	fashions
thought	solution	clothes	brother's
father	hopeful	those	include
uncomfortable	cough	incredible	pictures

DST 3, Form B: word endings/suffixes

children	neighbour	frightening	□	windows
centre		listening	sound	money
garden		situation	both	round
hear		awful	steal	together
mother's	□□	desperate	weak	either
discussion		prevent	friend	photo-graphs
telephone		terrible	definitely	fashions
thought		solution	clothes	brother's
father	□□	hopeful	those	include
uncomfort-able		cough	incredible	pictures

Diagnostic Spelling Tests photocopy master published by Hodder Murray

DST 3, Form B: sight words

children	neighbour	frightening	□	windows
centre	□	listening	sound	money
garden	□	situation	both	round
hear		awful	steal	together
mother's	□	desperate	weak	either
discussion		prevent	friend	photo-graphs
telephone		terrible	definitely	fashions
thought	□	solution	clothes	brother's
father		hopeful	those	include
uncomfort-able		cough	incredible	pictures

Diagnostic Spelling Tests photocopy master published by Hodder Murray

Diagnostic Spelling Test 3: follow-up diagnostic checks

Check 1: Medium-frequency words

My **friends** are very **important** to me.

I **heard** a **sound** outside the **window**.

I read **something** about that in yesterday's **paper**.

The **baby** is growing so quickly she needs bigger **clothes** already.

I borrowed some **money** from mum to buy a **birthday** present for my **brother**.

Are you sure you **don't** want to go **swimming**?

Our new house has only a **small garden**.

My little **sister** chose the **white balloon**.

The **children** were **happy** at Water World – they had a **great** time the **whole** weekend.

Check 2: homophones

I had a good half-term **break** last **week**, but the **weather** was dreadful. I was **sure** I would be **bored**, but mum **allowed** me to have friends round. One **night** she took us to the **fair** and we had good fun, even when it started to **pour** with **rain** and we had to run **through** huge puddles to get back to the car.

I like **cereal** for breakfast.

You need butter, sugar, eggs and **flour** to make a cake.

Try not to **waste** any fabric.

Stainless **steel** is a type of metal.

Use a ruler to draw a **straight** line under the title.

Could I have some **peace** and quiet, please?

The next **scene** is set in a forest.

Can everyone **hear** me?

Check 3: double consonants

Can you **carry** in the **supper** things please?

Discuss in your groups what **happened** when the three witches met on the heath.

The **assistant** came **running** when he thought we were leaving the shop.

I can't use the computer because I've **forgotten** my **password**.

We're doing **addition** problems in numeracy **tomorrow**.

My little sister painted a **pretty pattern**.

Our **holly** bush has lots of **berries** this year.

I went on a **tennis** course at the **beginning** of the holidays.

Check 4: common prefixes

Footballers can only **transfer** to a new club at certain times.

The **audience** clapped politely at the end of the play.

The new **supermarket** is enormous.

I was fascinated by the sharks at the **aquarium**.

The **aeroplane** was delayed because of heavy snow.

Next year I'll be able to ride my **bicycle** to school.

The **microphone** was faulty so it was difficult to hear the speaker clearly.

When I left **primary** school I missed my friends.

I like to watch **television** after school.

The race followed a **circular** route.

Check 5: suffixes and common word endings

The **optician** said I need to wear glasses when I read.

The house was destroyed by a gas **explosion**.

The **percussion section** had a huge variety of drums and gongs.

There's going to be an end-of-term **celebration**.

My class won the handwriting **competition**.

Alice drank the magic **potion** and fell down the rabbit-hole.

People are concerned about the **pollution** of rivers and the sea.

I felt **miserable** when I was too ill to see my friends.

Those trainers are far too **expensive**.

If **possible**, I would like to go bowling on Saturday.

On **completion** of our project, we had to take it to the headteacher.

Check 1: medium-frequency words

My _____ are very _____ to me.

I _____ a _____ outside the _____.

I read _____ about that in yesterday's _____.

The _____ is growing so quickly she needs bigger _____ already.

I borrowed some _____ from mum to buy a _____ present for my _____.

Are you sure you _____ want to go _____?

Our new house has only a _____

My little _____ chose the _____

The _____ were _____ at Water

_____ – they had a _____ time the _____ weekend.

Check 2: homophones

I had a good half-term _____ last _____, but

the _____ was dreadful. I was _____ I would

be _____, but mum _____ me to have friends

round. One _____ she took us to the _____

and we had good fun, even when it started to _____ with

_____ and we had to run _____ huge

puddles to get back to the car.

I like _____ for breakfast.

You need butter, sugar, eggs and _____ to make a cake.

Try not to _____ any fabric.

Stainless _____ is a type of metal.

Use a ruler to draw a _____ line under the title.

Could I have some _____ and quiet, please?

The next _____ is set in a forest.

Can everyone _____ me?

Diagnostic Spelling Tests photocopy master published by Hodder Murray

Check 4: common prefixes

Footballers can only _____ to a new club at certain times.

The _____ clapped politely at the end of the play.

The new _____ is enormous.

I was fascinated by the sharks at the _____.

The _____ was delayed because of heavy snow.

Next year I'll be able to ride my _____ to school.

The _____ was faulty so it was difficult to hear the speaker clearly.

When I left _____ school I missed my friends.

I like to watch _____ after school.

The race followed a _____ route.

Check 3: double consonants

Can you _____ in the _____ things please?

_____ in your groups what _____ when the three witches met on the heath.

The _____ came _____ when he thought we were leaving the shop.

I can't use the computer because I've _____ my _____.

We're doing _____ problems in numeracy _____.

My little sister painted a _____.

Our _____ bush has lots of _____ this year.

I went on a _____ course at the _____ of the holidays.

Diagnostic Spelling Tests photocopy master published by Hodder Murray

Check 5: suffixes and common word endings

The _____ said I need to wear glasses when I read.

The house was destroyed by a gas _____.

The _____ had a huge variety of drums and gongs.

There's going to be an end-of-term _____.

My class won the handwriting _____.

Alice drank the magic _____ and fell down the rabbit-hole.

People are concerned about the _____ of rivers and the sea.

I felt _____ when I was too ill to see my friends.

Those trainers are far too _____.

If _____, I would like to go bowling on Saturday.

On _____ of our project, we had to take it to the headteacher.

Diagnostic Spelling Tests photocopy master published by Hodder Murray

Diagnostic Spelling Test 4

The table below shows the sources of the words taken from the DfEE (2001) *Key Stage 3 National Strategy Framework for Teaching English: Years 7, 8 and 9*. Appendix 3 of the Framework comprises lists of words identified by secondary teachers as causing difficulties for students in Key Stage 3. The lists cover 'general' words which students might require in any curriculum subject, common homophones and confusions, and 'subject' words. The Framework recommends that students be helped to learn how to spell any words on these lists about which they are uncertain. As can be seen in the table below, *Diagnostic Spelling Test 4* includes words from all three lists.

	Form A	Form B
KS3 General list	audible	fierce
	straight	outrageous
	Wednesday	February
	development	permanent
	design	columns
	necessary	disappoint
	fulfil	skilful
	beautiful	daughter
	unfortunately	sincerely
	separate	definite
KS3 Common homophones	allowed	braking
	course	practice
KS3 Art	frieze	portrait
	exhibition	illusion
KS3 D & T	hygiene	protein
	recipe	portfolio
KS3 Drama	theatre	rehearse
	applause	dramatise
KS3 English	dialogue	grammar
	atmosphere	pamphlet
KS3 Geography	country	tourism
	region	erosion
KS3 History	disease	traitor
	parliament	agriculture
KS3 ICT	cursor	memory
	module	document
KS3 Library	dictionary	glossary
	catalogue	copyright
KS3 Mathematics	parallel	symmetrical
	circumference	percentage
KS3 Music	orchestra	choir
	rhythm	musician
KS3 PE	mobility	activity
	league	medicine
KS3 PSHE	generosity	dependency
	approval	ability
KS3 RE	commitment	celebration
	religious	prejudice
KS3 Science	laboratory	temperature
	amphibian	frequency

Test 4

dst

Following each 'script' to deliver the spelling test, below, is a table (page 39) to help you analyse Form A and Form B, categorising the words into different classifications. When marking a student's answers you may wish to check if there are any specific classifications where they show a marked strength or weakness. Annotated mark sheets with these classifications, as shown below, are provided on pages 40 and 41. These pages may be photocopied onto thermal transparencies to act as a quick way to check the analyses against the classifications.

The analysis of the words in the test is by the following categories:

Prefixes	Suffixes/word endings	With double consonant	Homophones	Key Stage 3: General list	KS3: Subject word lists
P	S	D	H	Words 1–10	Words 13–40

You will also see the *facility* for the question at the right of each line on which the students write their answer. This is the percentage of students in the standardisation trial that got this item correct. This information is there to help you make comparisons of an individual student's performance with the overall standardisation sample.

To utilise this method of analysis, students should answer on a copy of the answer sheet on page 91, as the overlays are designed to match to this answer sheet.

Giving the test

Diagnostic Spelling Test 4 is designed to be administered to whole classes or large groups, but may be used with individuals or small groups if this is preferred. It is provided in two parallel forms, A and B, to enable you to assess progress over time or after specific intervention.

Timing

No time limit is set for the test, but it is likely to take about 15 minutes for most groups. The test is paced by the person administering the test, as the items are read aloud to the students, but a fixed time of 15 seconds is allocated for answering. It is important that students complete the 40-word test in a single session.

Preparation

Each student will need a copy of the answer sheet, and writing materials. Test administrators should have a stop watch to enable them to monitor the 15-seconds timing.

Test conditions

It is important that the students work alone, without copying or discussing their answers. Answers may be altered by rubbing or crossing out.

Administration

Give each student a copy of the answer sheet: a photocopy master is provided on page 91. Introduce the test by telling them they should do their best to spell correctly the 40 words you are going to ask them to write. Tell them that there will be some words that they can spell easily, but that there are also some harder words. They should not worry if they find some difficult, but just try their best. Remind them to write as neatly and legibly as possible.

Example wording for administering the test is provided below, but this may be adapted – the most important thing is that the students understand what they have to do.

Ask the students to complete the details on the answer sheet – their name and gender, their date of birth and the date of testing – including the number (4) and the form (A or B) of the test to be given.

Marking

Once the student has completed the spelling test, their answers may be marked and, if required, analysed for diagnostic information. Mark each question as correct or incorrect, awarding one mark for each correct answer. If a student has made more than one attempt to spell a word, only mark the one that he or she has indicated is the final answer. If a word is illegible, check with the student if possible; otherwise, mark the word as incorrect.

- Scoring by students is not recommended, for even if papers are switched around to obviate any alterations, the scoring tends to be very inaccurate.
- Each correct word counts 1; no half-marks are allowed for 'nearly correct' or 'doubtful' answers.
- Omissions, like wrong spellings, count as zero.
- The correct part of speech is essential. For example, *column* is not accepted for *columns*; also *column's* is wrong.
- Ignore all capitalisations, regardless of whether they should be either present or absent (because of the sentence structure or if the word is a proper noun).
- Inserted hyphens (e.g. *ful-fil*) are wrong.
- If there is doubt about certain letters, they can usually be identified by comparing with the same letters in other words or you may check with the student if appropriate. Insertions are accepted if in the right place, but letter reversals are not.

The raw score should be recorded in the summary box on the top of the answer sheet. The student's chronological age on taking the test should be calculated in years and completed months. The standardised score, percentile and spelling age may then be found from the tables on pages 80–3.

Where students have not done well, their answers can be analysed to find if there are specific patterns of weakness. The categories identified for students of secondary school age and beyond are prefixes, suffixes, homophones, words with one or more double consonants and words from the KS3 general and subject words (*Key Stage 3 National Strategy Framework for Teaching English: Years 7, 8 and 9*, DfEE 2001).

Checking progress

Once you have determined the areas which need further teaching and reinforcement activities, you can utilise a variety of strategies to help your students improve their spelling. To assist teachers, some background on each of the analysis categories is given below. Pages 61–7 also include lists of words for some of the analysis categories which can be used in teaching.

To help you to check on a student's further progress, follow-up 'check' tests are provided on pages 42–3. These include focused tests on prefixes, suffixes and homophones, and general tests including words from across the categories. 'Scripts' giving the words in contextualised sentences for the teacher, teaching assistant or learning support assistant to read from, to deliver these tests, are also provided.

At a later stage, you may then wish to use the parallel form of the test to assess overall progress.

Students who attain very low scores

For older students who have attained very low scores, it is possible that their difficulties with spelling make an age-appropriate test unsuitable, in that an error analysis using only the categories listed above will not fully identify where their weaknesses lie. Also, there will be little indication of what spelling strategies the student can use accurately, or what phonic structures she or he knows.

In this situation, we suggest that you re-test using *Diagnostic Spelling Test 3*, which includes digraphs/trigraphs, medium-frequency words (from the National Literacy Strategy, DfES, 2001) and apostrophes in the error analysis, as well as prefixes, suffixes, homophones and words with double consonants. This will provide a fuller picture of the strategies the student is able to use effectively, as well as identifying those which need to be taught.

For very low attainers, *Diagnostic Spelling Test 2* may be suitable.

Clearly state the following:

I will tell you the number of the question, then I will read out each word. I will then read a sentence with the word in it. Finally I will repeat the word. You will have **fifteen seconds** in which to write the word by the correct number on the sheet. I will then go on to the next word.

1	audible	The quiet sound was still **audible**.	audible
2	straight	Use a ruler to draw a **straight** line.	straight
3	Wednesday	The day in the middle of the week is **Wednesday**.	Wednesday
4	development	We recorded the **development** of the caterpillar.	development
5	design	The artist drew a **design** for a silk jacket.	design
6	necessary	It was raining so an umbrella was **necessary** to keep dry.	necessary
7	fulfil	I hope he will **fulfil** his promise to be on time.	fulfil
8	beautiful	The garden looked **beautiful**.	beautiful
9	Unfortunately	**Unfortunately**, she had lost her keys so could not unlock the door.	Unfortunately
10	separate	The cook had to **separate** the white of the egg from the yolk.	separate
11	allowed	People wearing trainers were not **allowed** into the club.	allowed
12	course	The introductory **course** was just what he needed when he started the new job.	course
13	frieze	A decorative **frieze** ran round the top of the wall.	frieze
14	exhibition	There was an **exhibition** of paintings by local artists.	exhibition
15	hygiene	Good **hygiene** in the kitchen prevents food poisoning.	hygiene
16	recipe	Everyone liked the chef's new soup **recipe**.	recipe
17	theatre	The tourists went to see a play at the **theatre**.	theatre
18	applause	At the end of the song there was lots of **applause**.	applause
19	dialogue	The two actors had a long **dialogue** to learn for the play.	dialogue
20	atmosphere	The **atmosphere** in the room was hot and stuffy.	atmosphere
21	country	The bus was soon out of the city and into the **country**.	country
22	region	The map showed each **region** in a different colour.	region
23	disease	Years ago **disease** killed more babies than today.	disease
24	parliament	A new law was passed by the **parliament**.	parliament

Test 4

25	cursor	She moved the **cursor** with the mouse.	cursor
26	module	Each **module** was important to the complete system.	module
27	dictionary	Sam checked the spelling of the word in his **dictionary**.	dictionary
28	catalogue	Special low prices were given in the new **catalogue**.	catalogue
29	parallel	The railway lines were **parallel** with each other.	parallel
30	circumference	Steve used a compass to draw the **circumference** of a circle.	circumference
31	orchestra	My mother played the flute in an **orchestra**.	orchestra
32	rhythm	The drummers kept a steady **rhythm** as the band marched by.	rhythm
33	mobility	The lack of **mobility** of the wheelchairs did not affect the basketball game.	mobility
34	league	International footballers seem to be in a **league** of their own.	league
35	generosity	The **generosity** of the sponsors meant everyone could take part.	generosity
36	approval	The boss gave **approval** for the digging to start.	approval
37	commitment	The manager demanded total **commitment** from the team.	commitment
38	religious	The family was deeply **religious** and always prayed together.	religious
39	laboratory	The chemicals were stored in the **laboratory**.	laboratory
40	amphibian	A frog, as an **amphibian**, is able to live in water and on land.	amphibian

Clearly state the following:

I will tell you the number of the question, then I will read out each word. I will then read a sentence with the word in it. Finally I will repeat the word. You will have **fifteen seconds** in which to write the word by the correct number on the sheet. I will then go on to the next word.

1	fierce	The big dog was **fierce**.	fierce
2	outrageous	The price was **outrageous**.	outrageous
3	February	The shortest month of the year is **February**.	February
4	permanent	The stain on his shirt is **permanent** and will not wash out.	permanent
5	columns	The entrance is supported by four **columns** of marble.	columns
6	disappoint	The manager was sorry to **disappoint** the job applicant.	disappoint
7	skilful	Some golfers are very **skilful** at putting.	skilful
8	daughter	They were delighted with the birth of a **daughter**.	daughter
9	sincerely	He always liked to end his personal letters 'Yours **sincerely**'.	sincerely
10	definite	There was enough evidence to reach a **definite** conclusion.	definite
11	braking	The driver was continually **braking** to avoid the potholes.	braking
12	practice	The new dental **practice** is next to the health centre.	practice
13	portrait	I had my **portrait** painted.	portrait
14	illusion	He thought he saw a cool lake in the desert, but it was just an **illusion**.	illusion
15	protein	Meat is a good source of **protein**.	protein
16	portfolio	She kept all her drawings and plans in a **portfolio**.	portfolio
17	rehearse	The musicians had to **rehearse** for many hours.	rehearse
18	dramatise	He waved his arms around to **dramatise** what he was saying.	dramatise
19	grammar	Dave knew a lot of words in French, but his **grammar** was terrible.	grammar
20	pamphlet	The **pamphlet** was printed in bright colours.	pamphlet
21	tourism	The theme park increased **tourism** in the area.	tourism
22	erosion	Sand blowing on the cliff caused the **erosion**.	erosion
23	traitor	The police arrested the **traitor** who had been spying.	traitor

Test 4

24	agriculture	Using tractors instead of horses made a big difference to **agriculture** in the area.	agriculture
25	memory	The new computer had a huge **memory**.	memory
26	document	He finished typing and sent the **document** to the printer.	document
27	glossary	The words and their meanings were in the **glossary**.	glossary
28	copyright	To protect their design they added a **copyright** symbol at the bottom.	copyright
29	symmetrical	The two triangles were **symmetrical** in shape.	symmetrical
30	percentage	The charity distributed a large **percentage** of the money people had given.	percentage
31	choir	The **choir** sang beautifully.	choir
32	musician	The **musician** was playing a trumpet.	musician
33	activity	The hospital entrance buzzed with **activity**.	activity
34	medicine	Years ago, people thought **medicine** had to taste nasty to make you better.	medicine
35	dependency	Heroin addicts have a huge **dependency** on the drug.	dependency
36	ability	Some people have the **ability** to make friends easily.	ability
37	celebration	It was a great **celebration**, with food, music and fireworks.	celebration
38	prejudice	The company insisted there was no racial **prejudice** at the factory.	prejudice
39	temperature	She felt ill and had a very high **temperature**.	temperature
40	frequency	Bats hear high-**frequency** sound.	frequency

Morphemes

An awareness of morphemes becomes increasingly important to allow students to develop knowledge of words at the orthographic phase. Morphemes are the smallest chunks of words that carry meaning or grammatical information. So *international* has three morphemes *inter* (meaning 'between'), *nation* (meaning 'country') and *al* (indicating the adjectival form). It can be seen that if a student has never had to write *international* before, they are still likely to spell it accurately if they are familiar with the three constituent morphemes. The main morpheme in a word (in our instance *nation*) is often referred to as the 'base' or 'root' word. Morphemes added before this (e.g. *inter*) are 'prefixes', while those added afterwards (e.g. *al*) are suffixes.[4]

Other common sequences of letters that are not morphemes may also be remembered as chunks (for instance the *-ttle* in *bottle, kettle, rattle*), or spelled accurately by analogy with words that are known (for instance, if asked to spell the rare word *rimple*, we should be able to do so because of our knowledge of *simple* and *pimple*). We may also develop explicit strategies, such as using mnemonics, to remember sequences of letters in specific words.[5]

Prefixes

Prefixes are added at the beginnings of words to change their meanings (*anticlockwise, bicycle*). The same prefixes tend to occur in many different words, and so learning a relatively small number of them can make the spelling of a large number of words more accurate, including longer words and words not encountered before.

Suffixes

Suffixes are added to the ends of words to change their meaning or their grammatical function (*dishes, making, breakable*). As with prefixes, learning a relatively small number of them can make the spelling of a large number of words more accurate, including longer words and words not encountered before. The same is true of learning some other common word endings (*butter, kettle*) that are not strictly speaking suffixes.

Suffixing is not always purely a matter of adding a suffix to the end of a word. Sometimes letters need to be dropped (*make + ing = making*), extra letters added (*chat + ing = chatting*), or letters changed (*shelf + s = shelves*). Suffixes and suffixing rules in spelling form part of the NLS throughout

[4] A discussion of morphemic awareness and how children use this from quite an early point in their spelling development can be found in Nunes, T., Bryant, P. and Bindman, M. (1997) 'Morphological spelling strategies: developmental stages and processes', *Developmental Psychology*, *33*, 637–49.
[5] These issues are investigated in Ehri, L. (1997) 'Learning to Read and Learning to Spell are One and the Same, Almost', in Perfetti, C., Rieben, L. and Fayol, M. (eds.) *Learning to Spell: Research, Theory and Practice across Languages*, Lawrence Erlbaum.

Test 4

the primary phase and are re-visited in the *Framework for Teaching English*.

Diagnostic Spelling Test 4 includes many words with suffixes and other common word endings. By looking at student responses to these, it is possible to see whether:

- common suffixes and endings have been learned (e.g. *-s, -ed, -ing, -er, -est, -le, -sion, -al*);
- rules for combining these with base words have been learned or absorbed (doubling letters, etc);
- students are familiar with less common suffixes and endings (e.g. *-ment, -sion, -ism*).

Words with double consonants

One aspect of spelling that even quite advanced spellers find difficult is remembering whether specific words contain single or double consonants. These words fall roughly into two categories:

- those where there is a double consonant as the result of a suffixing rule;
- those where the double consonant forms part of a base word.

Diagnostic Spelling Test 4 includes examples of the latter type, eg *parallel* and *commitment*. Where this type of structure is problematic, it suggests students have not developed a feel for one of the patterns of English spelling, where double consonants usually indicate:

- the preceding vowel is a short vowel (*b<u>u</u>tter*, *r<u>a</u>bbit*); and
- the preceding syllable is stressed (the *butt-* of *butter* is pronounced more heavily than the *-er*).

However, although some phonics programmes advocate teaching this pattern (usually in terms of 'open' and 'closed' syllables), it is conceptually quite difficult for many students. It is probably better to explore visual strategies to help students have a distinctive image of the double letter in the word, or to use mnemonics.

Homophones

Homophones are words that sound the same but are spelled differently. Those in Test 4 are: *straight* (strait), *allowed* (aloud), *course* (coarse), *frieze* (freeze), *cursor* (curser), *choir* (quire), *braking* (breaking), *practice* (practise).

Where students provide the wrong spelling, it may indicate a number of things:

- They may not be familiar with the actual spelling and so are using their phonics to attempt the word (*strait* is phonologically more plausible than the actual spelling of *straight*). The fact that *strait* is a real word would be coincidental.
- They may be familiar with both words, but select the wrong one.

In the first instance, a memory for the actual spellings of words needs to be developed (see below, under *'Irregular' words*).

The second instance suggests the link between meaning and spelling is not sufficiently strong. It is important that words should be written, and read, in a meaningful context as much as possible, and it may also be useful to look explicitly at pairs of words and explore the meanings of each.

Subject words

These are words selected from those specified in the *Framework for Teaching English* as requiring a particular spelling focus in KS3. The intention is, therefore, that they should be learnt as 'sight words', where the exact sequence of letters is remembered, allowing the words to be spelled quickly and automatically. Students can then use them in their own writing without, for instance, having to make conscious use of phonics, and so allowing more attention to be given to the content of their writing.

Where a significant number of these words is misspelled on the test, it could indicate that insufficient attention is being given to the learning of them or that students are not being given sufficient opportunity to write (and so to use the words repeatedly in a meaningful context).

'Irregular' words

These are words that it would be particularly difficult to spell accurately through the straightforward application of phonics, and so have to be learned, at least to some extent, as 'sight words'.[6]

Where the actual sequence of letters has not been learned, but a student's basic phonics is good, misspellings are likely to be plausible – for instance *audible* spelled as *audable*, *catalogue* as *catalog*, or *copyright* as *copyrite*. This may suggest that although the alphabetic phase has been mastered in spelling, moving through the orthographic phase to acquire a large spelling vocabulary is proving problematic.

Teaching students how to learn sight words is often overlooked. Possible strategies include:

- *Visualisation* – the student looks at the word written in large letters, and then tries to see it inside their head, perhaps changing the colours of the letters or saying what letters they can see
- *Auditory strategies* – using spelling pronunciations (pronouncing the *d* in *Wednesday*, or the *ar* in gramm<u>ar</u>), or taping themselves saying aloud the sequence of letters in a word and then playing it back a number of times
- *Kinaesthetic strategies* – remembering the movement the hand makes when writing a word, by, for instance, using a finger to trace a number of times over a word written in large letters, then repeating the movement with a pencil

[6] There is a shifting line between what counts as irregular and what counts as regular, depending on the phonics patterns and rules taught, and the frequency of their occurrence. For instance, the *wr* in *wreck* may be taught as a digraph for the phoneme /r/, and so the word could be considered regular. Nevertheless, it would be unusual for a child to select *wr* as their first choice for spelling /r/. The 'irregular' words presented here are intended as a useful diagnostic selection.

■ *Mnemonics* – memory tricks usually using memorable sentences or phrases (*big elephants can all understand small elephants* = *because*), ideally made up by the students themselves.

Research suggests that it is beneficial to help students select their own best strategy for learning the spelling of 'sight words'.[7] Whichever strategy, or combination of strategies, is used, it is important that students develop a habit of checking spelling attempts when they are practising a word – otherwise they will often be reinforcing a misspelling of a word. Encouraging them to check each letter aloud in turn with a model written by a teacher can be helpful.

[7] Brooks, P. and Weekes, S. (1999) *Individual Styles in Learning to Spell: Improving Spelling in Children with Literacy Difficulties and all Children in Mainstream Schools*, DfEE Publications.

DST 4 Form B

	Prefixes	Suffixes/ word endings	With double consonant	Homophones	KS3 general list	KS3 subject lists
fierce						
outrageous	✓	✓			✓	
February		✓			✓	
permanent	✓	✓			✓	
columns		✓			✓	
disappoint	✓		✓		✓	
skilful		✓			✓	
daughter		✓			✓	
sincerely		✓			✓	
definite	✓				✓	
braking				✓		✓
practice				✓		✓
portrait		✓				✓
illusion	✓		✓			✓
protein	✓					✓
portfolio						✓
rehearse	✓					✓
dramatise		✓				✓
grammar			✓			✓
pamphlet						✓
tourism		✓				✓
erosion		✓				✓
traitor		✓				✓
agriculture						✓
memory		✓				✓
document		✓	✓			✓
glossary		✓	✓			✓
copyright						✓
symmetrical		✓				✓
percentage	✓					✓
choir				✓		✓
musician		✓				✓
activity						✓
medicine						✓
dependency	✓	✓				✓
ability						✓
celebration		✓				✓
prejudice	✓					✓
temperature						✓
frequency		✓				✓

DST 4 Form A

	Prefixes	Suffixes/ word endings	With double consonant	Homophones	KS3 general list	KS3 subject lists
audible		✓				
straight				✓	✓	
Wednesday		✓			✓	
development	✓	✓			✓	
design	✓		✓		✓	
necessary		✓			✓	
fulfil		✓			✓	
beautiful		✓			✓	
unfortunately	✓	✓			✓	
separate		✓			✓	
allowed		✓		✓	✓	
course				✓		
frieze				✓		
exhibition	✓	✓				✓
hygiene						✓
recipe						✓
theatre						✓
applause	✓		✓			✓
dialogue						✓
atmosphere						✓
country				✓		✓
region		✓				✓
disease						✓
parliament	✓	✓				✓
cursor		✓				✓
module		✓				✓
dictionary		✓				✓
catalogue						✓
parallel		✓	✓			✓
circumference	✓	✓				✓
orchestra						✓
rhythm		✓				✓
mobility		✓				✓
league						✓
generosity	✓	✓				✓
approval	✓	✓	✓			✓
commitment	✓	✓	✓			✓
religious	✓	✓				✓
laboratory		✓				✓
amphibian	✓					✓

Diagnostic Spelling Test 4, Form A: Analysis overlay

To enable analysis of spellings, the codes below show how each word is classified. The facility value – the % of students who got each spelling correct – is shown to the right of these codes.

Prefixes P (max 10)	Suffixes/ word endings S (max 20)	With double consonant D (max 6)	Homo- phones H (max 5)	KS3 general words Words 1–10 (max 10)	KS3 subject words Words 13–40 (max 28)

Word	No.	Code	Facility	No.	Code	Facility	Word
audible	1	S	0.23	21		0.91	country
straight	2	H	0.81	22	S	0.70	region
Wednesday	3	S	0.92	23	P	0.5	disease
development	4	PS	0.85	24	S	0.22	parliament
design	5	P	0.79	25	SH	0.37	cursor
necessary	6	SD	0.26	26	S	0.67	module
fulfil	7		0.11	27	S	0.78	dictionary
beautiful	8	S	0.74	28		0.36	catalogue
Unfortunately	9	PS	0.27	29	D	0.30	parallel
separate	10	S	0.29	30	PS	0.34	circumference
allowed	11	SH D	0.68	31		0.47	orchestra
course	12	H	0.77	32		0.21	rhythm
frieze	13	H	0.07	33	S	0.75	mobility
exhibition	14	SP	0.38	34		0.59	league
hygiene	15		0.26	35	S	0.40	generosity
recipe	16		0.54	36	PS D	0.56	approval
theatre	17		0.61	37	SD	0.53	commitment
applause	18	PD	0.57	38	PS	0.44	religious
dialogue	19		0.35	39		0.29	laboratory
atmosphere	20		0.71	40	P	0.43	amphibian

Diagnostic Spelling Tests photocopy master published by Hodder Murray

Diagnostic Spelling Test 4, Form B: Analysis overlay

To enable analysis of spellings, the codes below show how each word is classified. The facility value – the % of students who got each spelling correct – is shown to the right of these codes.

Prefixes P (max 10)	Suffixes/ word endings S (max 20)	With double consonant D (max 5)	Homo- phones H (max 3)	KS3 general words Words 1–10 (max 10)	KS3 subject words Words 13–40 (max 28)

word	#	S	D	val	#	H	gen	val	subject
fierce	1			0.55	21		S	0.66	tourism
outrageous	2		PS	0.34	22		S	0.52	erosion
February	3		S	0.44	23		S	0.44	traitor
permanent	4		PS	0.27	24			0.47	agriculture
columns	5		S	0.26	25			0.81	memory
disappoint	6		PD	0.15	26		S	0.86	document
skilful	7		S	0.11	27		SD	0.69	glossary
daughter	8		S	0.86	28			0.72	copyright
sincerely	9		S	0.29	29		SD	0.12	symmetrical
definite	10		P	0.16	30		P	0.80	percentage
braking	11		SH	0.38	31		H	0.55	choir
practice	12		H	0.61	32		S	0.52	musician
portrait	13			0.64	33			0.77	activity
illusion	14		PS D	0.58	34			0.55	medicine
protein	15		P	0.57	35		PS	0.38	dependency
portfolio	16			0.56	36			0.76	ability
rehearse	17		P	0.44	37		S	0.71	celebration
dramatise	18			0.68	38		P	0.15	prejudice
grammar	19		SD	0.39	39			0.56	temperature
pamphlet	20			0.12	40		S	0.64	frequency

Diagnostic Spelling Tests photocopy master published by Hodder Murray

Check 1: Prefixes

misfortune	He met one **misfortune** after another.	Y7 Spelling Bank: General
anticlockwise	Turn the screw **anticlockwise**.	Y7 Spelling Bank: General
immoral	Murder is both **immoral** and illegal.	KS3: R.E.
abduct	It is a crime to **abduct** a person.	Y7 Spelling Bank: General
microscopic	It was a **microscopic** particle.	Y7 Spelling Bank: General
bisects	The red line **bisects** the green line at its centre.	Y7 Spelling Bank: General
kilometre	Walk exactly one **kilometre** and time yourself.	KS3: Mathematics
almost	It is **almost** lunchtime.	Y7 Spelling Bank: General
audience	The **audience** loved the film.	Y7 Spelling Bank: General
triangle	Draw a **triangle**.	KS3: Mathematics

Check 2: Suffixes

revolutionary	The invention of the bicycle had a **revolutionary** effect.	KS3: History
originally	This house was **originally** built as a school.	Y7 Spelling Bank: General
subordinate	The employee was a **subordinate** of the big boss.	KS3: English
manufacture	Robots are used to **manufacture** cars.	KS3: D&T
dimension	Good use of colour adds an extra **dimension** to a painting.	KS3: Art
lighting	The **lighting** in the club was very dim.	KS3: Drama
location	Brownfield sites are the best **location** for new housing.	KS3: Geography
tournament	Our team came last in the **tournament.**	KS3: PE
friction	**Friction** slows you down.	KS3: Science
discussion	We will begin the **discussion** at 10.30.	KS3 PSHE

Check 3: Homophones

through	We have been **through** this problem before.	KS3 very high-frequency homophone
weight	Measure the **weight** of the ingredients accurately.	Y7 Spelling Bank: General
rode	She **rode** the winning horse.	KS3 very high-frequency homophone
dyed	She had **dyed** her hair red and green!	KS3: very high-frequency homophone
would	If I were you, I **would** tell them everything.	KS3: very high-frequency homophone
sew	I have to **sew** by hand for my Textiles project.	KS3: D and T
bytes	File size is measured in **bytes**.	KS3: ICT

weather	The unseasonal **weather** adversely affected the grape harvest.	KS3: Geography
current	I enjoy watching **current** affairs programmes.	KS3: History
minor	The melody was in a **minor** key.	KS3: Music

Check 4: General test A

approximately	The car park is **approximately** one hundred metres long.	KS3: Mathematics
communication	I have been in **communication** with the newspaper.	KS3: PSHE
thermometer	A **thermometer** is needed for many science experiments.	KS3: Science
rebellion	The soldiers were not able to stop the **rebellion**.	KS3: History
muscles	It is important to warm up your **muscles** before exercising.	KS3: PE
recurring	There is a **recurring** number in the solution to this division.	KS3: Mathematics
physical	Bricklaying is a **physical**, outdoors job.	Y7 Spelling Bank: General
beginning	New Year's Day is the **beginning** of the year.	Y7 Spelling Bank: General
librarian	Take your book to the **librarian** to get it stamped.	KS3: Library
write	I'll **write** to you when I arrive.	KS3: very high-frequency homophone

Check 5: General test B

irregular	The cake was an **irregular** shape.	KS3: Mathematics
collection	Samir had an extensive art **collection**.	KS3: Art
expression	The **expression** on her face was sad.	KS3: English
commandments	The ten **commandments** were proclaimed to the Hebrews.	KS3: RE
machine	The **machine** has broken down.	KS3: D&T
positive	In this calculation, you will need to add **positive** and negative numbers.	KS3: Mathematics
scene	The final **scene** of the play was the most exciting.	KS3: Drama
climb	It was a hard **climb** up the mountain.	Y7 Spelling Bank: General
marriage	After the couple's **marriage** there was a splendid reception.	Y7 Spelling Bank: General
pressure	It is often necessary to apply **pressure** to a bleeding wound.	KS3: Science

Diagnostic Spelling Test 5

The words in this test are those that are often spelled incorrectly by adults. They are not incredibly difficult words, nor are they ones that have particularly nasty surprises in them. Most can be correctly spelled by using basic spelling or phonological rules. As such, they may be deemed part of our functional literacy.

The table below shows the pairing of the words in Forms A and B. In assembling these tests we were informed by a variety of sources, including research conducted by Yell of the most commonly mis-spelled words in enquiries to their website, and words that journalists identified as being difficult to spell. We recognise that many people will have their own selection of favourites for including in such tests and we do not claim to have the definitive list of challenges in terms of functional literacy, but believe that the tests give a fair and thorough coverage of the various rules which help people spell effectively.

Form A	Form B	Form A	Form B
disappear	embarrass	exaggerate	immediate
believe	relief	request	queue
assessment	accommodation	glamorous	gorgeous
argument	continuous	achieve	receive
knowledge	guard	gauge	mortgage
potential	industrial	transferred	selected
participation	persuasion	scent	whether
unnecessary	occurred	extremely	library
grateful	successful	privileged	college
naturally	practically	certified	licence
persistent	independent	occasion	decision
effect	affected	criticism	enthusiasm
environment	government	paralysis	business
permanent	behaviour	oscillate	exercises
truancy	university	supervisor	envisage
optician	electrician	energetic	benefit
accepted	dissipated	abundance	experience
career	weird	similar	personal
simultaneous	tremendously	alienated	limited
excess	except	emptiness	variation

A number of commonly mis-spelled words are also to be found in *Diagnostic Spelling Test 4*, but in Test 4 three-quarters of the words are taken from the KS3 specific vocabulary lists of the major school subjects, so it is biased to what might be called technical/academic rather than functional literacy.

Following each 'script' to deliver the spelling test, below, is a table (page 56) to help you analyse Form A and Form B, categorising the words into different classifications. When marking a student's answers, you may wish to check if there are any specific classifications where they show a marked strength or weakness. Annotated mark sheets with these classifications, as shown below, are provided on pages 57 and 58. These pages may be photocopied onto thermal transparencies to act as a quick way to check the analyses against the classifications.

The analysis of the words in the test is by the following categories:

Prefixes	Suffixes/word endings	With double consonant	Homophones
P	S	D	H

You will also see the *facility* for the question at the right of each line on which the students write their answer. This is the percentage of students in the standardisation trial that got this item correct. This information is there to help you make comparisons of an individual student's performance with the overall standardisation sample.

To utilise this method of analysis, students should answer on a copy of the answer sheet on page 91, as the overlays are designed to match to this answer sheet.

Giving the test

Diagnostic Spelling Test 5 is designed to be administered to whole classes or large groups, but may be used with individuals or small groups if this is preferred. It is provided in two parallel forms, A and B, to enable you to assess progress over time or after specific intervention.

Timing

No time limit is set for the test, but it is likely to take about 15 minutes for most groups. The test is paced by the person administering the test, as the items are read aloud to the students, but a fixed time of 15 seconds is allocated for answering. It is important that students complete the 40-word test in a single session.

Preparation

Each student will need a copy of the answer sheet, and writing materials. Test administrators should have a stop watch to enable them to monitor the 15-seconds timing.

Test conditions

It is important that the students work alone, without copying or discussing their answers. Answers may be altered by rubbing or crossing out.

Administration

Give each student a copy of the answer sheet: a photocopy master is provided on page 91. Introduce the test by telling them they should do their best to spell correctly the 40 words you are going to ask them to write. Tell them that there will be some words that they can spell easily, but that there are also some harder words. They should not worry if they find some difficult, but just try their best. Remind them to write as neatly and legibly as possible.

Example wording for administering the test is provided below, but this may be adapted – the most important thing is that the students understand what they have to do.

Ask the students to complete the details on the answer sheet – their name and gender, their date of birth and the date of testing – including the number (5) and the form (A or B) of the test to be given.

Marking

Once the student has completed the spelling test, their answers may be marked and, if required, analysed for diagnostic information. Mark each question as correct or incorrect, awarding one mark for each correct answer. If a student has made more than one attempt to spell a word, only mark the one that he or she has indicated is the final answer. If a word is illegible, check with the student if possible; otherwise, mark the word as incorrect.

- Scoring by students is not recommended, for even if papers are switched around to obviate any alterations, the scoring tends to be very inaccurate.
- Each correct word counts 1; no half-marks are allowed for 'nearly correct' or 'doubtful' answers.
- Omissions, like wrong spellings, count as zero.
- The correct part of speech is essential. For example, *exercise* is not accepted for *exercises*; also *exercise's* is wrong.
- Ignore all capitalisations, regardless of whether they should be either present or absent (because of the sentence structure or if the word is a proper noun).
- Inserted hyphens (e.g. *ex-cept*) are wrong.
- If there is doubt about certain letters, they can usually be identified by comparing with the same letters in other words or you may check with the student if appropriate. Insertions are accepted if in the right place, but letter reversals are not.

The raw score should be recorded in the summary box on the top of the answer sheet. The student's chronological age on taking the test should be calculated in years and completed months. The standardised scores and percentiles may then be found from the tables on pages 86–9.

Where students have not done well, we suggest their answers are analysed to find if there are specific patterns of weakness. The categories identified are prefixes, suffixes, words with one or more double consonants and homophones.

Checking progress

Once you have determined the areas which need further teaching and reinforcement activities, you can utilise a variety of strategies to help your students improve their spelling. To assist teachers, some background on each of the analysis categories is given below. Pages 61–7 also include lists of words for some of the analysis categories which can be used in teaching.

To help you to check on a student's further progress, follow-up 'check' tests are provided on pages 59–60. These include focused tests on prefixes, suffixes and homophones, and general tests including words from across the categories. 'Scripts' giving the words in contextualised sentences for the teacher or learning support assistant to read from, to deliver these tests, are also provided.

At a later stage, you may then wish to use the parallel form of the test to assess overall progress.

Students who attain very low scores

For older students who have attained very low scores, it is possible that their difficulties with spelling make an age-appropriate test unsuitable, in that an error analysis using only the categories listed above will not fully identify where their weaknesses lie. Also, there will be little indication of what spelling strategies the student can use accurately, or what phonic structures she or he knows.

In this situation, we suggest that you re-test using *Diagnostic Spelling Test 3*, which includes digraphs/trigraphs, medium-frequency words (from the National Literacy Strategy, DfEE, 2001) and apostrophes in the error analysis, as well as prefixes, suffixes, homophones and words with double consonants. This will provide a fuller picture of the strategies the student is able to use effectively, as well as identifying those which need to be taught.

For very low attainers, *Diagnostic Spelling Test 2* may be suitable.

Clearly state the following:

I will tell you the number of the question, then I will read out each word. I will then read a sentence with the word in it. Finally I will repeat the word. You will have **fifteen seconds** in which to write the word by the correct number on the sheet. I will then go on to the next word.

1	disappear	The magician made the rabbit **disappear**.	disappear
2	believe	People used to **believe** that the earth is flat.	believe
3	assessment	The insurance company wanted an **assessment** of the damage.	assessment
4	argument	Nazim was cross because he lost the **argument** with his brother.	argument
5	knowledge	The book claimed to be full of **knowledge** for the reader.	knowledge
6	potential	She knew she could realise her **potential** if she trained harder.	potential
7	participation	Half-marathons are great **participation** events for all sorts of people.	participation
8	unnecessary	Molly said that it was **unnecessary** to shout at the dog.	unnecessary
9	grateful	Sita was **grateful** for the offer of babysitting.	grateful
10	naturally	Public speaking comes **naturally** for some people.	naturally
11	persistent	If you are **persistent**, you often get what you want.	persistent
12	effect	The **effect** of the earthquake could be seen for several kilometres.	effect
13	environment	There is concern that industry does not care enough for the **environment**.	environment
14	permanent	The advertisement claimed that the glue was **permanent**.	permanent
15	truancy	There is a concern about levels of **truancy**.	truancy
16	optician	People who wear glasses should go to the **optician** regularly.	optician
17	accepted	Claire **accepted** the change from the shop assistant without looking.	accepted
18	career	Jez wanted a **career** in banking.	career
19	simultaneous	When it's close, the flash and the bang from lightning are **simultaneous**.	simultaneous
20	excess	They had to pay extra for the **excess** baggage.	excess

Test 5

21	exaggerate	Do not **exaggerate** the size of the fish you caught.	exaggerate
22	request	The party-goers received a **request** from the neighbours for less noise.	request
23	glamorous	Film stars are so **glamorous**.	glamorous
24	achieve	I want to **achieve** success.	achieve
25	gauge	The pressure **gauge** was broken.	gauge
26	transferred	Fed up with being let down, she **transferred** her account to another bank.	transferred
27	scent	The **scent** of her perfume was overpowering.	scent
28	extremely	A desert is an **extremely** empty place.	extremely
29	privileged	**Privileged** customers get special treatment.	privileged
30	certified	Milk from **certified** herds is safer to drink.	certified
31	occasion	A wedding is a joyful **occasion**.	occasion
32	criticism	**Criticism** is never easy to accept.	criticism
33	paralysis	One effect of a stroke could be **paralysis** of an arm or leg.	paralysis
34	oscillate	The researchers watched the spot on the screen **oscillate** up and down.	oscillate
35	supervisor	Always report a workplace hazard to your **supervisor**.	supervisor
36	energetic	On holiday it was too hot to be **energetic**.	energetic
37	abundance	It was a good year for fruit; we had an **abundance** of plums.	abundance
38	similar	The twins had **similar** views on politics.	similar
39	alienated	Her outspokenness **alienated** her from her colleagues.	alienated
40	emptiness	Following the breakdown of their relationship, he felt a great **emptiness**.	emptiness

Clearly state the following:

I will tell you the number of the question, then I will read out each word.
I will then read a sentence with the word in it. Finally I will repeat the
word. You will have **fifteen seconds** in which to write the word by the
correct number on the sheet. I will then go on to the next word.

1	embarrass	John would often **embarrass** his sister by acting the fool.	embarrass
2	relief	'What a **relief** to get home,' said the old man.	relief
3	accommodation	The view from the hotel was fantastic and the **accommodation** was amazing.	accommodation
4	continuous	The road across the desert looked like a **continuous** black line.	continuous
5	guard	The soldiers stood on **guard** outside the palace.	guard
6	industrial	Technology companies worry about **industrial** spies stealing their latest ideas.	industrial
7	persuasion	It did not take much **persuasion** to get Sasha to join the group.	persuasion
8	occurred	A brilliant idea **occurred** to Josh.	occurred
9	successful	The team of pensioners was always **successful** at bowls.	successful
10	practically	For most people, singing in tune is **practically** impossible.	practically
11	independent	Going to university helps you to become **independent**.	Independent
12	affected	She was not **affected** by the delay.	affected
13	government	Good local **government** should improve the area we live in.	government
14	behaviour	Parents expect good **behaviour** from their children.	behaviour
15	university	Many students take a year out before going to **university**.	university
16	electrician	The lights all went out, so we phoned for an **electrician**.	electrician
17	dissipated	She shouted and shouted until all her anger was **dissipated**.	dissipated
18	weird	Green hair looks **weird** on most men.	weird
19	tremendously	The suitcase was **tremendously** heavy.	tremendously
20	except	They all wore white trainers **except** Zahir, who wore black ones.	except
21	immediate	He needed an **immediate** answer.	immediate
22	queue	She joined the **queue** to buy her rail ticket.	queue

Test 5

23	gorgeous	The meal was **gorgeous**.	gorgeous
24	receive	I love to **receive** presents.	receive
25	mortgage	She took out a **mortgage** to buy her first flat.	mortgage
26	selected	Evelyn was **selected** to play for the hockey team.	selected
27	whether	James did not know **whether** to accept the invitation to dinner with his new boss.	whether
28	library	Books can be borrowed from a **library**.	library
29	college	**College** is a great place to gain further qualifications.	college
30	licence	Once you pass your test, you get a full driving **licence**.	licence
31	decision	The first **decision** of the committee was to agree their expenses.	decision
32	enthusiasm	Employers look for **enthusiasm** in their trainees.	enthusiasm
33	business	A successful **business** makes a profit.	business
34	exercises	They warmed up for the race by doing **exercises**.	exercises
35	envisage	The workforce did not **envisage** being made redundant.	envisage
36	benefit	Most people will **benefit** from more exercise.	benefit
37	experience	Work **experience** is a good way to check out a possible career.	experience
38	personal	Life style is a very **personal** choice.	personal
39	limited	The holiday discount was available for a **limited** time.	limited
40	variation	In Moscow, there is a great **variation** in the temperature.	variation

Morphemes

An awareness of morphemes becomes increasingly important to allow students to develop knowledge of words at the orthographic phase. Morphemes are the smallest chunks of words that carry meaning or grammatical information. So *international* has three morphemes *inter* (meaning 'between'), *nation* (meaning 'country') and *al* (indicating the adjectival form). It can be seen that if a student has never had to write *international* before, they are still likely to spell it accurately if they are familiar with the three constituent morphemes. The main morpheme in a word (in our instance *nation*) is often referred to as the 'base' or 'root' word. Morphemes added before this (e.g. *inter*) are 'prefixes', while those added afterwards (e.g. *al*) are suffixes.[8]

Other common sequences of letters that are not morphemes may also be remembered as chunks (for instance the *–ttle* in *bottle, kettle, rattle*), or spelled accurately by analogy with words that are known (for instance, if asked to spell the rare word *rimple*, we should be able to do so because of our knowledge of *simple* and *pimple*). We may also develop explicit strategies, such as using mnemonics, to remember sequences of letters in specific words.[9]

Prefixes

Prefixes are added at the beginnings of words to change their meanings (<u>anti</u>clockwise, <u>bi</u>cycle). The same prefixes tend to occur in many different words, and so learning a relatively small number of them can make the spelling of a large number of words more accurate, including longer words and words not encountered before.

Suffixes

Suffixes are added to the ends of words to change their meaning or their grammatical function (*dis<u>hes</u>, mak<u>ing</u>, break<u>able</u>*). As with prefixes, learning a relatively small number of them can make the spelling of a large number of words more accurate, including longer words and words not encountered before. The same is true of learning some other common word endings (*butt<u>er</u>, kett<u>le</u>*) that are not strictly speaking suffixes.

Suffixing is not always purely a matter of adding a suffix to the end of a word. Sometimes letters need to be dropped (*mak<u>e</u> + ing = making*), extra letters added (*chat + ing = chat<u>t</u>ing*), or letters changed (*shelf + s = shel<u>ves</u>*). Suffixes and suffixing rules in spelling form part of the NLS throughout the primary phase and are re-visited in the *Framework for Teaching English*.

[8] A discussion of morphemic awareness and how children use this from quite an early point in their spelling development can be found in Nunes, T., Bryant, P. and Bindman, M. (1997) 'Morphological spelling strategies: developmental stages and processes', *Developmental Psychology*, *33*, 637-49.
[9] These issues are investigated in Ehri, L. (1997) 'Learning to Read and Learning to Spell are One and the Same, Almost', in Perfetti, C., Rieben, L. and Fayol, M. (eds.) *Learning to Spell: Research, Theory and Practice across Languages*, Lawrence Erlbaum.

Test 5

Diagnostic Spelling Test 5 includes many words with suffixes and other common word endings. By looking at student responses to these, it is possible to see whether:

- common suffixes and endings have been learned (e.g. *-s, -ed, -ing, -er, -est, -le, -sion, -al*);
- rules for combining these with base words have been learned or absorbed (doubling letters, etc);
- students are familiar with less common suffixes and endings (e.g. *-ment, -ism*).

Words with double consonants

One aspect of spelling that even quite advanced spellers find difficult is remembering whether specific words contain single or double consonants. *Diagnostic Spelling Test 5* has included a number of words containing double consonants. These words fall roughly into two categories:

- those where there is a double consonant as the result of a suffixing rule (e.g. *natura<u>ll</u>y, transfe<u>rr</u>ed*);
- those where the double consonant forms part of a base word (e.g. *exa<u>gg</u>erate, osci<u>ll</u>ate, a<u>ff</u>ected*).

Where the first of these is proving difficult, further exploration of suffixing is needed (see above). Where the second type is problematic, it suggests students have not developed a feel for one of the patterns of English spelling, where double consonants usually indicate:

- the preceding vowel is a short vowel (*b<u>u</u>tter, r<u>a</u>bbit*); and
- the preceding syllable is stressed (the *butt-* of *butter* is pronounced more heavily than the *-er*).

However, although some phonics programmes advocate teaching this pattern (usually in terms of 'open' and 'closed' syllables), it is conceptually quite difficult for many students. It is probably better to explore visual strategies to help students have a distinctive image of the double letter in the word, or to use mnemonics.

Homophones

Homophones are words that sound the same but are spelled differently. Those in *Diagnostic Spelling Test 5* are: *effect* (affect), *accepted* (excepted), *whether* (weather), *licence* (license), *affected* (effected), *except* (accept), *queue* (cue), *gauge* (gage), *scent* (sent).

Where students provide the wrong spelling, it may indicate a number of things:

- They may not be familiar with the actual spelling and so are using their phonics to attempt the word (*sent* and *cue* are both phonologically more plausible than the actual spelling of *scent* and *queue*). The fact that *sent* and *cue* are real words would be coincidental.
- They may be familiar with both words, but select the wrong one.

When homophones, as shown by the example of *scent* and *queue*, are answered incorrectly, a memory for the actual spellings of words, together with their meanings, needs to be developed (see below, under *'Irregular' words*).

Sight words

These are words selected here as appropriate to the adult working environment. The intention is therefore that they should be learnt as 'sight words', where the exact sequence of letters is remembered, allowing the words to be spelled quickly and automatically. Students can then use them in their own writing without, for instance, having to make conscious use of phonics, and so allowing more attention to be given to the content of their writing.

Where a significant number of these words are misspelled on the test, it could indicate that insufficient attention is being, or has ever been, given to the learning of them or that students are not being given sufficient opportunity to write (and so to use the words repeatedly in a meaningful context).

'Irregular' words

These are words that it would be particularly difficult to spell accurately through the straightforward application of phonics, and so have to be learned, at least to some extent, as 'sight words'.

Where the actual sequence of letters has not been learnt, but a student's basic phonics is good, misspellings are likely to be plausible – for instance *knowledge* spelled as *nolige* or *supervisor* as *supaviser*. This may suggest that although the alphabetic phase has been mastered in spelling, moving through the orthographic phase to acquire a large spelling vocabulary is proving problematic.

Teaching students how to learn sight words is often overlooked. Possible strategies include:

- *Visualisation* – the student looks at the word written in large letters, and then tries to see it inside their head, perhaps changing the colours of the letters or saying what letters they can see
- *Auditory strategies* – using spelling pronunciations (pronouncing the *w* in *kno__w__ledge*, or saying *busy-ness* for *business*), or taping themselves saying aloud the sequence of letters in a word and then playing it back a number of times
- *Kinaesthetic strategies* – remembering the movement the hand makes when writing a word, by, for instance, using a finger to trace a number of times over a word written in large letters, then repeating the movement with a pencil
- *Mnemonics* – memory tricks usually using memorable sentences or phrases (*__big__ __e__lephants __c__an __a__ll __u__nderstand __s__mall __e__lephants* = *because*, or *there is no ass in occasion*); ideally they are made up by the students themselves.

Research suggests that it is beneficial to help students select their own best strategy for learning the spelling of 'irregular words'.[10]

Whichever strategy, or combination of strategies, is used, it is important that students develop a habit of checking spelling attempts when they are practising a word – otherwise they will often be reinforcing a misspelling of a word. Encouraging them to check each letter aloud in turn with a model written by a teacher or instructor can be helpful.

[10] Brooks, P. and Weekes, S. (1999) *Individual Styles in Learning to Spell: Improving Spelling in Children with Literacy Difficulties and all Children in Mainstream Schools*, DfEE Publications

Test 5

DST 5, Form A

DST 5, Form A	Prefixes	Suffixes/common word endings	Words with double consonant	Homophones
disappear	✓		✓	
believe				
assessment		✓	✓	
argument		✓		
knowledge				
potential		✓		
participation		✓		
unnecessary	✓	✓	✓	
grateful		✓		
naturally		✓	✓	
persistent	✓	✓		
effect			✓	✓
environment	✓	✓		
permanent	✓			
truancy				
optician		✓		
accepted	✓	✓	✓	✓
career		✓		
simultaneous		✓		
excess	✓		✓	
exaggerate	✓		✓	
request	✓			
glamorous		✓		
achieve				
gauge				✓
transferred	✓	✓	✓	
scent				✓
extremely	✓	✓		
privileged		✓		
certified		✓		
occasion	✓	✓	✓	
criticism		✓		
paralysis				
oscillate			✓	
supervisor	✓	✓		
energetic	✓	✓		
abundance		✓		
similar				
alienated		✓		
emptiness		✓	✓	

DST 5, Form B

DST 5, Form B	Prefixes	Suffixes/common word endings	Words with double consonant	Homophones
embarrass	✓		✓	
relief	✓			
accommodation	✓	✓		
continuous	✓	✓		
guard				
industrial	✓	✓		
persuasion	✓	✓		
occurred	✓	✓	✓	
successful		✓	✓	
practically		✓	✓	
independent	✓	✓		
affected	✓	✓	✓	✓
government		✓		
behaviour				
university	✓			
electrician		✓		
dissipated	✓	✓	✓	
weird				
tremendously		✓		
except	✓			✓
immediate	✓		✓	
queue				✓
gorgeous		✓		
receive	✓			
mortgage				
selected		✓		
whether				✓
library				
college			✓	
licence				✓
decision	✓	✓		
enthusiasm	✓	✓		
business			✓	
exercises	✓	✓		
envisage	✓			
benefit				
experience	✓	✓		
personal	✓	✓		
limited		✓		
variation		✓		

Diagnostic Spelling Test 5, Form A: Analysis overlay

To enable analysis of spellings, the codes below show how each word is classified. The facility value – the % of students who got each spelling correct – is shown to the right of these codes.

Prefixes P (max 14)	Suffixes/ word endings S (max 23)	With double consonant D (max 12)	Homophones H (max 4)

Word	#		Code	Facility	#		Code	Facility	Word
disappear	1		PD	0.67	21		PD	0.56	exaggerate
believe	2			0.92	22		P	0.97	request
assessment	3		SD	0.64	23		S	0.43	glamorous
argument	4		S	0.70	24			0.84	achieve
knowledge	5			0.93	25		H	0.52	gauge
potential	6		S	0.94	26		PS D	0.72	transferred
participation	7		S	0.89	27		H	0.90	scent
unnecessary	8		PS D	0.51	28		PS	0.73	extremely
grateful	9		S	0.68	29		S	0.13	privileged
naturally	10		SD	0.88	30		S	0.89	certified
persistent	11		P	0.40	31		PS D	0.76	occasion
effect	12		DH	0.97	32		S	0.69	criticism
environment	13		PS	0.83	33			0.55	paralysis
permanent	14		P	0.64	34		D	0.27	oscillate
truancy	15			0.59	35		PS	0.87	supervisor
optician	16		S	0.75	36		PS	0.94	energetic
accepted	17		PS DH	0.94	37		S	0.75	abundance
career	18			0.83	38			0.93	similar
simultaneous	19		S	0.63	39		S	0.93	alienated
excess	20		PD	0.91	40		SD	0.70	emptiness

Diagnostic Spelling Test 5, Form B: Analysis overlay

To enable analysis of spellings, the codes below show how each word is classified. The facility value – the % of students who got each spelling correct – is shown to the right of these codes.

Prefixes P (max 20)	Suffixes/ word endings S (max 22)	With double consonant D (max 10)	Homophones H (max 5)

Word	#	Code	Facility	#	Code	Facility	Word
embarrass	1	PD	0.16	21	PD	0.77	immediate
relief	2	P	0.90	22	H	0.70	queue
accommodation	3	PS D	0.19	23	S	0.29	gorgeous
continuous	4	PS	0.78	24	P	0.43	receive
guard	5		0.92	25		0.76	mortgage
industrial	6	PS	0.95	26	S	0.97	selected
persuasion	7	PS	0.53	27	H	0.80	whether
occurred	8	PS D	0.41	28		0.88	library
successful	9	SD	0.72	29	D	0.89	college
practically	10	SD	0.81	30	H	0.32	licence
independent	11	PS	0.37	31	PS	0.80	decision
affected	12	PS DH	0.90	32	PS	0.86	enthusiasm
government	13	S	0.91	33	D	0.86	business
behaviour	14		0.88	34	PS	0.86	exercises
university	15	P	0.91	35	P	0.77	envisage
electrician	16	S	0.82	36		0.85	benefit
dissipated	17	PS D	0.34	37	PS	0.88	experience
weird	18		0.67	38	PS	0.97	personal
tremendously	19	S	0.78	39	S	0.98	limited
except	20	PH	0.87	40	S	0.94	variation

Diagnostic Spelling Tests photocopy master published by Hodder Murray

Check 1: Prefixes

antibiotic	Use some **antibiotic** cream on that cut.
irresponsible	He is too **irresponsible** to be given that task.
abdicate	Edward VII chose to **abdicate** so that he could marry Mrs. Simpson.
superseded	The model 10 will be **superseded** by the new model 11.
aerodynamic	This car has an **aerodynamic** design.
circulate	Please **circulate** this information to all your colleagues.
telepathy	It is believed that some people can communicate by using **telepathy**.
bilingual	He is **bilingual**, speaking both English and Urdu.
adjacent	The offices are **adjacent** to the factory building.
almighty	I heard an **almighty** crash!

Check 2: Suffixes

dietician	A **dietician** will advise you on the best food for your condition.
legible	Her handwriting is clear and **legible**.
transfusion	He required a blood **transfusion** after the accident.
mercifully	**Mercifully**, no one was hurt in the fire.
thoughtless	That was a **thoughtless** action.
plentiful	There are **plentiful** supplies of stationery in the cupboard.
petition	We are organising a **petition** to keep the local hospital open.
manageable	It is a **manageable** project for someone of your ability.
fiercest	That was the **fiercest** storm I have ever experienced!
supplier	Please contact the **supplier** to tell him the products were late arriving.

Check 3: Homophones

too	Don't be in **too** much of a hurry!
sighed	She **sighed** with relief when the project was finished.
threw	He **threw** in the best suggestion at the end of the meeting.
which	I am unsure **which** task to tackle first.
you're	**You're** in with a good chance of promotion!
passed	I **passed** her in the corridor only yesterday.
elicit	The chairperson tried to **elicit** everyone's ideas.
role	Your **role** within the department is increasingly important.
ensure	Please **ensure** that all desks are cleared on Wednesdays for cleaning.
plain	It is **plain** to see who is in charge here.

Test 5

Check 4: General test A

encountered	I **encountered** no difficulties with this task.
impatient	Alex had always been an **impatient** person.
specified	The project leader **specified** the exact requirements for the job.
principle	In **principle**, I agree with you.
current	It is important to keep up with **current** developments in the industry.
volunteered	Louisa **volunteered** to work at the weekend.
they're	I do not think **they're** qualified for the job.
miscellaneous	The file was full of **miscellaneous** papers.
rhythmically	He tapped **rhythmically** on the desk while he waited.
definite	There has been a **definite** improvement in working relations.
referred	The solicitor **referred** to her legal documents.
parliament	**Parliament** was about to break for the summer recess.

Check 5: General test B

declared	Nathan was **declared** the winner.
outspoken	Ali had always been an **outspoken** supporter of innovation.
multiplied	The workforce has **multiplied** considerably over the last few years.
formerly	The company was **formerly** known as Steel Fabrications Ltd.
passed	Jamila was pleased to have **passed** her driving test.
employed	The local factory **employed** at least fifty workers.
two	He thought his line manager was **two**-faced.
questionnaire	Please complete this **questionnaire.**
wholly	I **wholly** agree with your proposal.
separate	We must **separate** these two liquids for this experiment.
travelled	Andy had **travelled** around Europe before starting work.
agriculture	Working in **agriculture** can mean long hours on some days.

Word lists for reinforcement work following Tests 4 and 5

Prefixes

ac-: accede, accelerate, accent, accept, accessible, accessory, accident, accompany, according, account, accumulate, accurate, accusation, acknowledge, acquaintance, acquire, acquittal

af-: affect, affidavit, affiliate, affirmative, affix, affliction, affluent, afford, affront

ap-: apparatus, appeal, appearance, appendix, applaud, appliance, applicant, appreciate, apprehensive, approach, appropriate, approval, approximate

agri-: agricultural, agrimotor

as-: assault, assembly, assent, assertive, assessment, assignation, assignment, assist, association, assumption, assurance

amphi-: amphibian, amphibious, amphitheatre

be-: become, bedraggled, before, begin, behave, behind, belated, beleaguered, believe, belittle, below, beneath, bequest, bereaved, betray, between, beware

bene-: benefactor, beneficial, benefit, benevolent

cata-: cataclysm, catalogue, catalyst, catapult, cataract, catarrh, catastrophe

circum-: circumference, circumnavigate, circumscribe, circumspect, circumstances, circumstantial, circumvent

coll-: collaborate, collage, collapse, collate, collection, college, collision, colloquial

con-: concave, conceal, concede, conceive, concise, conclude, concrete, concussion, condescend, condition, confectionery, conference, confidential, confiscate, conflict, conform, congestion, congratulations, conjunction, connective, conquer, consequences, conservation, consider, consonant, construction, consumer, contemporary, contestant, continuous, conversation, conviction

de-: debase, decapitate, decay, deceive, decelerate, decipher, declare, decline, decompose, decontaminate, decrease, deface, default, deficit, defy, dehumanise, delete, demilitarised, demoralised, deny, departure, deprive, describe, despise, destroy, devalue, development

dis-: disagree, disappear, disappoint, disassemble, discover, discuss, disease, disfigure, dislike, disobey, disperse, display, disrupt, dissipate, dissolve, distort, distrust

dia-: diabetic, diagnosis, diagonal, diagram, dialect, dialogue, dialysis, diameter, diaphragm

Prefixes cont.

ef-	en-	ex-	il-	im-	in-	oc-	out-	para-	per-	pre-
effective	enable	excellent	illegal	imbalance	inaccurate	occasion	outcast	parable	perceive	preamble
effervescent	enact	except	illicit	immaculate	inadequate	occluded	outer	parabola	perception	precaution
efficient	enamel	exceptional	illiterate	immaterial	inanimate	occupation	outing	parachute	percolate	precedent
effigy	encircle	excessive	illuminated	immature	inappropriate	occupy	outlaw	paradigm	percussion	precocious
effort	enclose	exchange	illusion	immediately	inaudible	occur	outlet	paradox	peremptory	preconceived
effrontery	encounter	excursion	illustration	immense	incandescent		outlying	paragraph	perennial	predecessor
effusive	encourage	exercise	illustrious	immigration	incapable		outnumber	parallel	perfect	predict
	encroach	exhibition		imminent	incendiary		outpatient	parallelogram	performance	predisposed
	endemic	exile		immobile	incentive		outrageous	paralysis	perforated	pre-empt
	endurance	expel		immoderate	incident		outright	parameter	perfume	prefabricated
	enemy	experience		immoral	incisive		outside	paranoia	permanent	preface
	energy	explode		immune	include		outspoken	parapet	permanganate	prefix
	enjoyment	export		impact	incompetent		outworker	paraphernalia	permeate	prehistoric
	enrich	extend		impair	increase			paraphrase	permit	prejudice
	ensure	external		impartial	indefinite			parasite	perpetrator	preliminary
	enthusiastic	extreme		impassable	indent				persecute	prelude
	enunciate			impassive	indicative				persevere	premature
	envelop			impatient	indigestion				perspective	preparation
	envious			impeccable	individual				perspex	prepaid
	envisage			impediment	indolent				persuade	presume
	enzyme			imperative					perturbed	preview
				imperceptible					pervasive	previous
				impermeable					pervious	
				impersonate						
				impervious						
				impossible						
				impoverish						
				improbable						

Prefixes *cont.*

pro-	re-	succ-	sym-	trans-	un-	uni-
proceed	reaction	succeed	symbol	transaction	unable	unicycle
procession	rebellious	success	symmetry	transatlantic	unacceptable	unilateral
procrastinate	rebuild	successive	sympathy	transfer	unbalanced	unicorn
produce	recall	succinct	symphony	transform	uncertain	uniform
production	recede	succulent	symposium	translucent	undone	unique
professional	receive	succumb	symptom	transparent	unearth	unison
professor	recognise			transplant	unfair	unite
profile	recommend			transport	unfortunate	universal
profit	recreate				unfriendly	
profound	recycled				unhappy	
programme	reduce				unkind	
progress	reference				unlocked	
prohibited	reflection				unnatural	
projector	reflex				unnecessary	
prologue	reform				unpleasant	
prolong	refraction				unpopular	
prominent	refrigerate				unselfish	
promise	refund				unsettled	
promote	regurgitate				untidy	
pronounce	reject				untie	
propagate	relegated				unusual	
propeller	remainder				unwell	
proportion	remember				unwrap	
proposition	removal					
prosecute	repair					
prospectus	repeated					
protection	represent					
proverb	reputation					
provide	resign					
provoke	retaliate					
	reveal					
	revolve					

super-

superficial
superfluous
superhero
superintendent
supermarket
supernatural
superpower
supersonic
supervisor

Suffixes/common word endings

-tion	-ation	-etion / -ition	-otion / -ution	-ssion / -sion	-sion	-cian / other 'shun' endings	-al	-ial
addiction	accommodation	-etion	-otion	-ssion	Same spelling pattern but different pronunciation:	-cian	agricultural	artificial
attention	alliteration	completion	emotion	depression		dietician	alphabetical	financial
combustion	calculation	deletion	lotion	discussion	collision	electrician	approval	industrial
conjunction	celebration	depletion	motion	expression	conclusion	magician	cathedral	material
connection	circulation		notion	mission	confusion	musician	chemical	official
construction	classification	-ition	potion	passion	corrosion	optician	chronological	partial
contradiction	communication	addition		percussion	decision	politician	constitutional	potential
description	concentration	ambition	-ution	permission	division		emotional	social
digestion	condensation	competition	constitution	possession	erosion	other 'shun' endings	equilateral	special
direction	education	composition	evolution	oppression	explosion	fashion	exceptional	
fiction	evaluation	exhibition	pollution	session	fusion	ocean	festival	
fraction	evaporation	preposition	resolution		illusion	Russian	horizontal	
function	examination	proposition	revolution	-sion	invasion	suspicion	interval	
production	explanation			dimension	persuasion		mammal	
proportion	illustration			extension	provision		mineral	
reflection	imagination			mansion	revision		national	
section	improvisation			pension	supervision		natural	
subtraction	information			suspension	television		original	
	innovation			extension	transfusion		personal	
	investigation						physical	
	invitation						regional	
	multiplication						rehearsal	
	participation						rural	
	personification						symmetrical	
	preparation						theatrical	
	presentation						traditional	
	respiration						vertical	
	rotation						vocal	
	situation							
	specification							
	syncopation							
	transportation							
	variation							

Suffixes/common word endings cont.

-ance
abundance, brilliance, circumstance, irrelevance, performance, relevance

-ence
audience, circumference, conscience, consequence, defence, evidence, independence, intelligence, persistence, preference, presence, reference, sequence

-ary
anniversary, arbitrary, centenary, contrary, diary, dictionary, estuary, February, glossary, honorary, imaginary, library, necessary, primary, revolutionary, salary, secondary, stationary, tertiary, vocabulary, voluntary

-ar
cellar, circular, grammar, irregular, particular, regular, spectacular, triangular

-er
computer, daughter, December, diameter, examiner, manager, passenger, polyester, publisher, quaver, scanner, server, shoulder, supplier, teenager, weather

-or
conductor, cursor, denominator, director, editor, incisor, major, metaphor, minor, monitor, narrator, predator, processor, sector, sensor, traitor, translator

-ate
aggravate, alternate, anticipate, calculate, candidate, co-ordinate, decapitate, estimate, immediate, indeterminate, isolate, exaggerate, facilitate, magistrate, navigate, oscillate, precipitate, primate, relate, separate, terminate, translate

-cy
buoyancy, constancy, dependency, frequency, truancy, vibrancy

-age
adage, average, breakage, courage, coverage, damage, discourage, dotage, encourage, homage, marriage, mileage, percentage, postage

-able
achievable, believable, breakable, comparable, employable, enjoyable, impenetrable, inexcusable, knowledgeable, manageable, parable, portable, probable, reliable, valuable, variable, vegetable

-ible
audible, discernible, edible, horrible, illegible, incredible, irresistible, possible, responsible, sensible, terrible

-ice
apprentice, avarice, cowardice, jaundice, justice, malice, notice, novice, practice, precipice, service

-ise
advise, colonise, compromise, dramatise, exercise, franchise, improvise, maximise, merchandise, minimise, pressurise, prioritise, revise, supervise, sympathise, synchronise

Suffixes/common word endings cont.

-day	-ic	-ing	-ism	-ity	-ment	-ory	-re	-ule	-ly
today	acrylic	beginning	baptism	ability	argument	auditory	centimetre	capsule	actually
yesterday	aesthetic	braking	extremism	activity	assessment	compulsory	centre	globule	approximately
+ days of the week	athletic	burying	organism	agility	development	laboratory	fibre	granule	beautifully
	atomic	deciding	pragmatism	amenity	document	memory	kilometre	module	carefully
	chromatic	defying	sexism	authority	employment	perfunctory	litre		completely
	dynamic	enjoying	specialism	city	engagement	sensory	metre		definitely
	electronic	enveloping	tourism	electricity	enjoyment		pressure		extremely
	fabric	happening		generosity	environment		theatre		fully
	frantic	hoping		immorality	government				happily
	graphic	justifying		majority	imprisonment				lonely
	gymnastic	kidnapping		minority	movement				lovely
	historic	listening		morality	ornament				naturally
	horrific	pulling		possibility	parliament				normally
	lyric	slimming		practicality	statement				occasionally
	metallic	winning		publicity					practically
	organic			purity					quickly
	rhythmic			opportunity					successfully
	specific			reality					traditionally
	supersonic			relativity					tremendously
	traffic			responsibility					unfortunately
				solidity					wholly
				sustainability					

-ent	-is	-ite	-iour	-ness	-ous	-ture	-ful	-asm
adjacent	analysis	ammonite	behaviour	awareness	conscious	agriculture	beautiful	chasm
benevolent	dialysis	composite	saviour	business	continuous	culture	careful	enthusiasm
competent	emphasis	definite		carelessness	generous	furniture	dreadful	spasm
component	osmosis	dynamite		emptiness	glamorous	future	graceful	
equivalent	paralysis	erudite		fitness	jealous	horticulture	grateful	
intelligent	synthesis	expedite		happiness	marvellous	infrastructure	hopeful	
malevolent	thesis	graphite		illness	miscellaneous	literature	painful	
permanent		unite		kindness	nervous	manufacture	peaceful	
persistent				readiness	outrageous	suture	pitiful	
translucent				silliness	religious	temperature	plentiful	
transparent				unpleasantness	simultaneous	texture	successful	
							wonderful	

Double consonants

abbreviate	arrangement	effective	letter	scanner
accept	assessment	efficient	litter	specially
accessory	assistant	embarrass	mammal	stress
accommodation	beginning	expression	narrative	success
actually	business	following	necessary	suddenly
addition	cannon	formally	occasion	suffering
address	collect	grammar	parallel	suffix
affordable	colloquial	guess	passenger	suggest
aggravate	comma	happen	password	surrender
aggressive	comment	illegible	pattern	swimming
allegory	commitment	illiterate	pollution	terrific
alliteration	common	illustration	possession	tomorrow
apparatus	concession	immediate	pretty	wettest
appear	connect	imminent	processor	
applause	correct	innovation	programme	
application	dessert	interrupt		
appoint	different			
approve	discussion			
approximate				

Homophones

accept/except	herd/heard	rein/reign/rain
affect/effect	here/hear	review/revue
aloud/allowed	hoard/horde	right/rite/write
aural/oral	idle/idol	role/roll
bail/bale	knew/new	scene/seen
bare/bear	knight/night	sew/sow
board/bored	know/no	shear/sheer
brake/break	larva/lava	site/sight
caught/court	lead/led	stationary/stationery
cereal/serial	leant/lent	steel/steal
check/cheque	licence/license	strait/straight
complement/compliment	lightening/lightning	sure/shore
course/coarse	loath/loathe	taut/taught
currant/current	marshal/martial	there/their/they're
dependent/dependant	meter/metre	threw/through
draft/draught	passed/past	tire/tyre
dual/duel	peace/piece	vain/vein
elicit/illicit	place/plaice	waist/waste
ensure/insure	plain/plane	waive/wave
faint/feint	practise/practice	weak/week
fair/fare	principal/principle	weather/whether
flour/flower		who's/whose
formally/formerly		your/you're
freeze/frieze		

Development and standardisation

Prior to the standardisation trials, the authors worked with the Learning Support team of Coventry LEA, who gave much valuable advice which enabled us to refine and revise the original drafts.

Between September and December 2005, over 4500 pupils, students and trainees took part in the standardisation trials for Forms A and B of the *Diagnostic Spelling Tests 1–5*: the schools and organisations involved are listed in the acknowledgements at the front of the manual. The sample includes various types of schools and training organisations from different parts of England to ensure that the sample was fairly representative of the students in education. The table below indicates the numbers of students at each age that formed the final Secondary/adult sample.

The Secondary/adult standardisation sample

Year		Form A Average total marks			Form B Average total marks			Numbers of students		
cohort	Test	Males	Females	Total	Males	Females	Total	Males	Females	Total
7	3	29.23	30.48	29.82	28.58	31.07	29.75	138	122	260
7	4	16.98	17.06	17.02	17.41	16.83	17.12	107	104	211
8	4	18.34	21.22	19.74	18.60	21.54	20.03	126	119	245
9	4	20.17	22.28	21.19	20.46	22.46	21.43	123	114	237
10	4	23.02	22.44	22.72	22.67	21.16	21.90	48	50	98
10	5	28.06	24.10	27.46	27.50	26.77	27.39	169	30	199
11	4	29.50	26.80	28.27	25.92	26.10	26.00	12	10	22
11	5	27.96	27.19	27.86	28.05	30.12	28.31	176	26	202
12	5	32.68	29.69	32.18	32.02	31.06	31.86	174	35	209
13	5	32.44	32.29	32.41	32.12	33.29	32.32	130	28	158
Trainees	5	24.26	10.00	24.08	25.26	12.00	25.09	77	1	78
Totals for Test 3 (inc. Years 5, 6 and 7)								639	554	1193
Totals for Test 4 (inc. Years 7, 8, 9, 10 and 11)								416	397	813
Totals for Test 5 (inc. Years 10, 11, 12, 13 and trainees)								726	120	846

Validity and reliability

The *validity* of the tests for use in English schools is assured by their close match with the National Literacy Strategy and the *Framework for Teaching English: Years 7, 8 and 9*. The design of the tests ensures that all of the words the pupils meet will most likely have been covered during the two- or three-year period the test is designed to check.

The *reliability* of a test indicates whether or not we would get similar results from repeated administrations of the test with similar samples of students. An appropriate measure of test reliability for the *Diagnostic Spelling Tests* is Cronbach's Alpha (α), which measures internal consistency reliability. Test theory tells us that test reliability is also related to test length, and suggests that any test should comprise at least 30 items to achieve reasonable reliability. In fact, all forms of the *Diagnostic Spelling*

Tests comprise 40 items (target words), so we expect their test reliabilities to be high: the values in the following table confirm this expectation.

Test	Number of students in standardisation sample	Number of items (target words) in test	Cronbach's Alpha (α) reliability
Test 3: Form A	1193	40	0.94
Test 3: Form B	1193	40	0.95
Test 4: Form A	813	40	0.93
Test 4: Form B	813	40	0.92
Test 5: Form A	846	40	0.90
Test 5: Form B	846	40	0.88

The age-standardisation process

Age-standardised test scores take into account a student's age, so that we have an indication of how each student is performing relative to other students of the same age. The objective of the age-standardisation process was to produce a look-up table with columns classified across the top by age (in years and completed months) and rows by test raw score. Each cell of the table contains a *standardised score* value which represents the raw score adjusted for the student's age.

The average standardised score for each age group is 100, with a standard deviation of 15. This means that if a student achieves a standardised score of 100, then that student has average ability for his or her age. About two-thirds of students will have standardised scores between 85 and 115. About 16% of students will be above 115 and the remaining 16% will be below 85 (see also pages 71–2).

The validity of the age standardisation is improved if there is a good correlation between students' raw test scores and age. Additionally, the test itself must have high reliability (internal consistency – see above) so that the results would be replicated by repeated administrations of the test.

For tests targeting a particular age range, we use a standardisation method based on *percentile norms*, the fundamental principle being that scores at the same percentile rank are comparable. Hence a student at, say, the 30th percentile in his/her age group has the same relative ability for their age as a student at the 30th percentile in any other age group. Raw scores would be expected to rise with students' ages, the older students tending to score more highly. The standardisation procedure used for these tests is the *non-parallel linear regression model*.[11]

[11] Our basic methodology follows D. G. Lewis (see *Statistical Methods in Education*, University of London Press, 1972, pp.86–96), with enhancements outlined by I. Schagen (see 'A method for the age standardisation of test scores', *Applied Psychological Measurement*, *14*, 4, December 1990, pp387–93) and L. A. Kiek, (*ESITEMS User Guide – Age Standardisation*, Cambridge University Local Examinations Syndicate, Research and Evaluation Division, 1997, p 61.)

Conversion tables

What do the scores mean?

Spelling ages

Spelling age is used by many teachers as a quick reference: a spelling age shows the *average* chronological age of the students who obtained each particular raw score – i.e. the chronological age at which this level of performance is typical. For more detailed comparative information, however, standardised scores and percentiles are to be preferred. Spelling ages have severe limitations with older students and adults (see page 73).

Standardised scores and percentiles

The technical information reported above indicates that the performance data provided by the tests is both robust and reliable. However, spelling age norms do not adequately convey the *significance* of scores above or below the average or median. For example, if a student scores a spelling age one year above, or two years below, his or her chronological age, it is not clear *how* superior or inferior these scores actually are. To gain a better feel for the *significance* of a student's spelling age, standardised scores and percentiles are more useful.

The relationship between standardised scores and percentiles is most easily seen by reference to Figure 1.

The **standardised scores** provided by the *Diagnostic Spelling Tests* range between 70 and 130, and the mean is 100. The vertical bands, determined by the standard deviation (SD) of 15, enable you to group students into:

- those whose performance is within an age-appropriate range (within one SD either side of the mean: i.e. 85–115);
- those who are below or above average in this regard (between one and two SDs either side of the mean: i.e. 70–85 and 115–130);
- those who are *well* below/*well* above the average for their age (between two and three SDs either side of the mean: i.e. below 70 or above 130).

Percentiles give alternative information concerning a student's performance in comparison to his or her age group. They show the *percentage* of the group from whom norms were obtained, which scored *below* the student's standardised score. So a standardised score at the 68th percentile is comfortably within the average range, since it means that 68 per cent of the group scored below the student's standardised score. A standardised score at the 16th percentile, however, means that only 16 per cent had a lower result. Scores below the 16th percentile (i.e. two standard deviations below the mean) are of concern, as they indicate performance that is well below average.

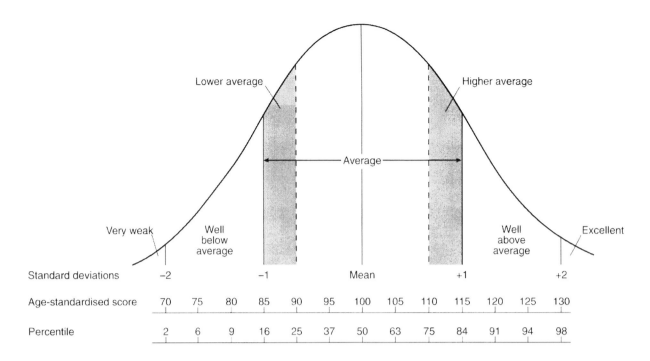

Standardised score	Qualitative interpretation of standardised scores	Standard deviation from mean	Percentile score	Percentage of normal population
>130	Excellent	>+2	>98	2.27
116–130	Well above average	+1 to +2	84–98	13.59
110–115 85–115 *85–90*	*higher average* Average/age-appropriate *lower average*	–1 to +1	16–83	68.26
70–84	Well below average	–1 to –2	2–15	13.59
<69	Very weak	<–2	<2	2.27

Figure 1: Relationship between standardised test scores and qualitative interpretations

To use the percentiles tables, first determine the student's age in years and completed months on the date they took the test. Locate this row in the table and look across it to find the score of correct spellings that they obtained. The heading of this column is the student's percentile score.

Item facilities

You may also go one stage further and check a student's individual performance on a specific spelling and compare how they have performed relative to other students in the same year group.

The Item Facilities tables show what proportion of students in each year group spelt each word correctly. This is called the *facility* and is shown as a decimal: a facility value of 0.6 means 60% of students answered the question correctly. It also helps you to find which spellings students, on average, found difficult and how performance improves with age and experience.

Inspection of the average facilities for each Year and overall for the tests indicates that Form A and Form B are parallel tests. Therefore either test form may be used and the tables of spelling ages, percentiles and standardised scores are the same for each.

Diagnostic Spelling Test 3: Spelling Ages

Number of words spelled correctly	Spelling Age	Number of words spelled correctly	Spelling Age
1–19	*below 9:0*	28	10:6
20	9:0	29	10:9
21	9:1	30	10:11
22	9:3	31	11:2
23	9:6	32	11:5
24	9:8	33	11:7
25	9:11	34	11:10
26	10:1	35+	12:0+
27	10:4		

Diagnostic Spelling Test 4: Spelling Ages

Number of words spelled correctly	Spelling Age	Number of words spelled correctly	Spelling Age
1–14	*below 11:0*	22	13:8
15	11:0	23	14:1
16	11:2	24	14:5
17	11:7	25	14:11
18	12:0	26	15:3
19	12:6	27	15:8
20	12:10	28+	16:0+
21	13:3		

Diagnostic Spelling Test 5: Spelling Ages

The table shows the very limited value spelling ages have for older secondary-age students and adults. It also exemplifies the risk of using spelling ages when most people have reached close to the plateau of their spelling capability, in that a score of just one more mark or one less mark is able to alter the spelling age by between one and two whole years. It is recommended that spelling ages are *not* reported from Test 5.

Number of words spelled correctly	Spelling Age
1–27	*below 14:0*
28	14:0
29	14:4
30	15:3
31	16:2
32	17:0
33	17:11
34+	18:0+

Diagnostic Spelling Test 3: Percentiles

| | | | | | | | | | | Percentile | | | | | | | | | | |
Age	5%	10%	15%	20%	25%	30%	35%	40%	45%	50%	55%	60%	65%	70%	75%	80%	85%	90%	95%	Age
9:0	2	6	8	11	12	14	15	17	19	20	22	23	24	26	27	29	31	32	34	9:0
9:1	3	6	9	11	13	14	16	17	19	21	22	23	25	26	28	29	31	33	34	9:1
9:2	3	6	9	11	13	15	16	18	20	21	22	24	25	26	28	29	31	33	34	9:2
9:3	3	7	10	12	14	15	17	18	20	21	23	24	25	27	28	29	31	33	35	9:3
9:4	4	7	10	12	14	15	17	19	20	22	23	24	26	27	28	30	31	33	35	9:4
9:5	4	8	10	13	14	16	18	19	21	22	23	25	26	27	29	30	32	33	35	9:5
9:6	4	8	11	13	15	16	18	19	21	22	24	25	26	27	29	30	32	34	35	9:6
9:7	5	8	11	14	15	17	18	20	21	23	24	25	27	28	29	31	32	34	35	9:7
9:8	5	9	12	14	16	17	19	20	22	23	25	26	27	28	29	31	32	34	35	9:8
9:9	6	9	12	14	16	18	19	21	22	24	25	26	27	28	30	31	33	34	35	9:9
9:10	6	10	12	15	17	18	20	21	23	24	25	26	28	29	30	31	33	34	36	9:10
9:11	6	10	13	15	17	18	20	22	23	24	26	27	28	29	30	31	33	34	36	9:11
10:0	7	10	13	16	17	19	20	22	23	25	26	27	28	29	31	32	33	35	36	10:0
10:1	7	11	14	16	18	19	21	22	24	25	26	28	28	30	31	32	33	35	36	10:1
10:2	7	11	14	17	18	20	21	23	24	25	27	28	29	30	31	32	34	35	36	10:2
10:3	8	11	15	17	19	20	22	23	25	26	27	28	29	30	31	33	34	35	36	10:3
10:4	8	12	15	17	19	21	22	24	25	26	27	29	29	30	32	33	34	35	37	10:4
10:5	8	12	15	18	20	21	22	24	25	27	28	29	30	31	32	33	34	36	37	10:5
10:6	9	13	16	18	20	21	23	24	26	27	28	29	30	31	32	33	35	36	37	10:6
10:7	9	13	16	19	20	22	23	24	26	27	28	30	30	31	33	34	35	36	37	10:7
10:8	9	13	17	19	21	22	23	25	27	28	29	30	31	32	33	34	35	36	37	10:8
10:9	10	14	17	20	21	23	24	26	27	28	29	30	31	32	33	34	35	36	37	10:9
10:10	10	14	17	20	22	23	25	26	27	28	30	31	31	32	33	34	35	37	37	10:10
10:11	10	15	18	20	22	24	25	26	28	29	30	31	32	33	34	35	36	37	38	10:11
11:0	11	15	18	21	23	24	25	27	28	29	30	31	32	33	34	35	36	37	38	11:0
11:1	11	15	19	21	23	24	26	27	28	30	31	32	32	33	34	35	36	37	38	11:1
11:2	11	16	19	22	23	25	26	28	29	30	31	32	33	33	34	35	36	37	38	11:2
11:3	12	16	20	22	24	25	27	28	29	30	31	32	33	34	35	36	36	37	38	11:3
11:4	12	17	20	23	24	26	27	28	30	31	32	33	33	34	35	36	37	38	38	11:4
11:5	12	17	20	23	25	26	27	29	30	31	32	33	34	35	35	36	37	38	39	11:5
11:6	13	17	21	23	25	26	28	29	30	31	32	33	34	35	36	36	37	38	39	11:6
11:7	13	18	21	24	25	27	28	30	30	32	33	34	34	35	36	37	37	38	39	11:7
11:8	13	18	22	24	26	27	29	30	31	32	33	34	35	35	36	37	38	38	39	11:8
11:9	14	19	22	25	26	28	29	30	31	32	33	34	35	36	36	37	38	39	39	11:9
11:10	14	19	22	25	27	28	29	31	32	33	34	35	35	36	37	37	38	39	39	11:10
11:11	14	19	23	25	27	29	30	31	32	33	34	35	36	36	37	38	38	39	40	11:11

Test 3

Diagnostic Spelling Test 3: Standardised scores

Age in years and completed months

Raw Score	10:5	10:4	10:3	10:2	10:1	10:0	9:11	9:10	9:9	9:8	9:7	9:6	9:5	9:4	9:3	9:2	9:1	9:0	Raw Score
1										70–	70–	70	71	71	72	72	73	74	1
2							70–	70–	70–	71	71	72	72	73	73	74	75	75	2
3				70–	70–	70–	70	71	71	72	73	73	74	74	75	76	76	77	3
4	70–	70–	70–	70	71	71	72	72	73	74	74	75	75	76	77	77	78	79	4
5	70	71	71	72	72	73	73	74	74	75	76	76	77	78	79	79	80	81	5
6	72	72	73	73	74	74	75	75	76	76	77	78	79	80	80	81	81	82	6
7	73	73	74	74	75	76	76	77	78	78	79	80	81	81	82	82	83	83	7
8	74	75	75	76	76	77	78	79	79	80	81	81	82	82	83	83	84	84	8
9	76	76	77	77	78	79	80	80	81	81	82	82	83	84	84	85	85	86	9
10	77	78	79	79	80	81	81	82	82	83	83	84	84	85	85	86	86	87	10
11	79	80	80	81	81	82	82	83	83	84	84	85	86	86	87	87	88	88	11
12	80	81	81	82	82	83	84	84	85	85	86	86	87	87	88	88	89	89	12
13	82	82	83	83	84	84	85	85	86	86	87	87	88	89	89	90	90	91	13
14	83	83	84	84	85	85	86	87	87	88	88	89	89	90	90	91	91	92	14
15	84	85	85	86	86	87	87	88	88	89	89	90	91	91	92	92	93	93	15
16	85	86	86	87	88	88	89	89	90	90	91	91	92	92	93	93	94	94	16
17	87	87	88	88	89	89	90	90	91	92	92	93	93	94	94	95	95	96	17
18	88	88	89	90	90	91	91	92	92	93	93	94	94	95	95	96	96	97	18
19	89	90	90	91	91	92	93	93	94	94	95	95	96	96	97	97	98	98	19
20	91	91	92	92	93	93	94	94	95	96	96	97	97	98	98	99	99	99	20
21	92	92	93	94	94	95	95	96	96	97	97	98	98	99	99	100	100	101	21
22	93	94	94	95	96	96	97	97	98	98	99	99	100	100	101	101	102	102	22
23	95	95	96	96	97	98	98	99	99	100	100	101	101	102	102	103	103	104	23
24	96	97	97	98	98	99	99	100	101	101	102	102	103	103	104	104	105	105	24
25	98	98	99	99	100	100	101	102	102	103	103	104	104	105	105	106	106	107	25
26	99	100	100	101	102	102	103	103	104	104	105	105	106	106	107	107	108	108	26
27	101	101	102	103	103	104	104	105	105	106	106	107	107	108	108	109	109	109	27
28	103	103	104	104	105	105	106	107	107	108	108	108	109	109	110	110	111	111	28
29	104	105	106	106	107	107	108	108	109	109	110	110	110	111	111	112	112	113	29
30	106	107	107	108	108	109	109	110	110	111	111	112	112	113	113	114	114	114	30
31	108	109	109	110	110	111	111	112	112	113	113	114	114	114	115	115	116	116	31
32	110	111	112	112	112	113	113	114	114	115	115	116	116	117	117	118	118	118	32
33	112	113	113	114	114	115	115	116	117	117	118	118	118	119	119	120	120	121	33
34	115	115	116	116	117	118	118	119	119	120	120	121	122	123	123	124	125	125	34
35	118	118	119	119	120	121	123	123	123	124	125	125	126	126	127	127	128	128	35
36	121	122	123	124	125	126	126	127	127	128	129	129	130	130+	130+	130+	130+	130+	36
37	127	127	128	129	129	130	130+	130+	130+	130+	130+	130+	130+						37
38	130+	130+	130+	130+	130+	130+													38
39																			39
40																			40
Raw Score	10:5	10:4	10:3	10:2	10:1	10:0	9:11	9:10	9:9	9:8	9:7	9:6	9:5	9:4	9:3	9:2	9:1	9:0	Raw Score

Age in years and completed months

Age in years and completed months

Raw Score	11:11	11:10	11:9	11:8	11:7	11:6	11:5	11:4	11:3	11:2	11:1	11:0	10:11	10:10	10:9	10:8	10:7	10:6	Raw Score
1																			1
2																			2
3																			3
4																			4
5																70–	70–	70–	5
6															70–	70	71	71	6
7														70–	71	71	72	72	7
8								70–	70–	70–	70–	70–	70–	70	72	73	73	74	8
9					70–	70–	70–	70	71	71	70	71	71	72	73	74	74	75	9
10			70–	70–	70	71	71	71	72	72	72	72	73	73	75	75	76	76	10
11	70–	70–	70	71	71	72	72	73	73	74	73	73	74	74	76	77	77	78	11
12	71	71	72	72	72	73	73	74	74	75	74	75	75	76	78	78	79	80	12
13	72	72	73	73	74	74	75	75	76	76	75	76	76	77	79	80	81	81	13
14	73	73	74	74	75	75	76	76	77	77	77	77	78	79	81	81	82	82	14
15	74	75	75	75	76	76	77	78	78	79	78	79	80	80	82	82	83	84	15
16	75	76	76	77	77	78	79	79	80	81	80	80	81	81	83	84	84	85	16
17	76	77	78	78	79	80	80	81	81	82	81	82	82	83	84	85	85	86	17
18	78	79	79	80	80	81	81	82	82	83	82	83	83	84	86	86	87	87	18
19	80	80	81	81	82	82	83	83	84	84	84	85	85	85	87	88	88	89	19
20	81	81	82	82	83	83	84	84	85	85	85	87	86	86	88	89	89	90	20
21	82	83	83	84	84	85	85	86	86	86	86	88	87	88	90	90	91	91	21
22	83	84	84	85	85	86	86	87	88	88	87	89	88	89	91	92	92	93	22
23	84	85	85	86	87	87	88	88	89	89	89	91	90	90	92	93	94	94	23
24	86	86	87	87	88	88	89	90	90	91	90	92	91	92	94	94	95	96	24
25	87	88	88	89	89	90	90	91	92	92	91	94	93	93	95	96	97	97	25
26	88	89	89	90	91	91	93	93	93	94	93	95	94	95	97	98	98	99	26
27	90	90	91	92	92	93	94	94	95	95	94	97	96	96	98	99	100	100	27
28	91	92	93	93	94	94	95	96	96	97	96	98	97	98	100	101	101	102	28
29	93	93	94	95	95	96	97	97	98	99	98	100	99	99	102	103	103	104	29
30	94	95	96	97	97	98	99	99	100	101	99	102	101	101	104	105	105	106	30
31	96	97	98	98	99	100	100	101	102	103	101	104	103	103	106	107	107	108	31
32	98	99	100	100	101	102	103	103	104	105	103	106	105	105	108	109	109	110	32
33	100	101	102	103	103	104	105	106	106	107	105	108	107	107	110	111	111	112	33
34	103	103	104	105	106	107	107	108	109	109	108	110	109	109	112	113	114	114	34
35	105	106	107	108	108	109	110	110	111	112	110	113	111	112	115	116	116	117	35
36	108	109	109	110	111	112	113	113	114	115	113	115	114	114	118	119	120	120	36
37	111	112	113	114	114	115	116	117	118	118	115	116	117	118	124	124	125	126	37
38	115	116	117	118	119	120	121	122	124	125	119	120	121	122	129	130	130+	130+	38
39	120	122	125	125	126	127	128	129	130	130+	126	127	127	128	130+	130+			39
40	130	130	130+	130+	130+	130+	130+	130+	130+		130+	130+	130+	130+					40
	11:11	11:10	11:9	11:8	11:7	11:6	11:5	11:4	11:3	11:2	11:1	11:0	10:11	10:10	10:9	10:8	10:7	10:6	

Age in years and completed months

Test 3

Diagnostic Spelling Test 3: Item facilities, by Year group

FORM A	Year 5	Year 6	Year 7	Overall	FORM B	Year 5	Year 6	Year 7	Overall
swimming	.85	.92	.99	.91	children	.86	.92	.95	.90
brother	.91	.95	.99	.94	centre	.42	.55	.65	.52
sister	.92	.94	.98	.94	garden	.87	.93	.93	.91
except	.36	.59	.68	.52	hear	.79	.86	.94	.85
inside	.88	.89	.98	.90	mother's	.21	.28	.23	.25
draughty	.12	.17	.13	.14	discussion	.20	.39	.48	.33
know	.78	.89	.94	.86	telephone	.67	.80	.90	.77
automatic	.47	.62	.73	.59	thought	.70	.84	.85	.79
relieved	.15	.26	.36	.24	father	.65	.75	.86	.73
session	.30	.49	.62	.44	uncomfortable	.24	.36	.47	.33
miserable	.31	.45	.56	.42	neighbour	.31	.47	.50	.41
eyes	.86	.89	.93	.89	listening	.49	.63	.73	.59
freight	.08	.19	.26	.16	situation	.45	.64	.72	.58
station	.64	.75	.87	.73	awful	.35	.47	.58	.45
direction	.59	.72	.84	.70	desperate	.27	.40	.55	.38
familiar	.22	.28	.42	.29	prevent	.68	.78	.77	.74
route	.41	.55	.74	.54	terrible	.55	.64	.71	.62
between	.67	.78	.89	.76	solution	.33	.53	.64	.47
different	.48	.68	.82	.63	hopeful	.53	.66	.77	.63
view	.55	.71	.78	.66	cough	.53	.67	.73	.63
stationary	.39	.54	.57	.49	frightening	.36	.53	.57	.47
excessive	.11	.25	.33	.21	sound	.85	.91	.99	.90
applied	.39	.50	.64	.49	both	.78	.88	.96	.86
brake	.62	.72	.73	.68	steal	.50	.63	.75	.61
work	.86	.91	.98	.90	weak	.72	.82	.91	.80
collision	.17	.31	.44	.28	friend	.69	.80	.91	.78
white	.85	.92	.97	.90	definitely	.05	.08	.10	.07
paper	.90	.93	.96	.92	clothes	.61	.72	.78	.69
earth	.77	.88	.95	.85	those	.68	.77	.86	.75
important	.63	.78	.82	.73	incredible	.50	.62	.68	.59
whole	.73	.79	.88	.79	windows	.86	.93	.98	.92
world	.81	.86	.93	.85	money	.84	.91	.99	.90
minister	.67	.71	.85	.73	round	.88	.92	.98	.91
previewed	.45	.58	.77	.57	together	.80	.87	.95	.86
memorable	.22	.38	.42	.33	either	.44	.62	.72	.57
audience	.30	.46	.57	.42	photographs	.55	.71	.87	.68
primary	.70	.82	.88	.79	fashions	.50	.60	.75	.65
shaming	.73	.79	.78	.77	brother's	.17	.26	.16	.20
careless	.66	.77	.88	.75	include	.58	.74	.81	.69
superpowers	.76	.85	.95	.84	pictures	.61	.71	.89	.71
Average facility	**.56**	**.66**	**.75**	**.64**	Average facility	**.55**	**.67**	**.74**	**.64**

Diagnostic Spelling Test 4: Percentiles

Age	5%	10%	15%	20%	25%	30%	35%	40%	45%	50%	55%	60%	65%	70%	75%	80%	85%	90%	95%	Age
										Percentile										
11:0	0	2	4	6	7	9	11	13	14	15	17	18	20	22	24	26	27	29	32	11:0
11:1	0	2	4	6	8	10	11	13	14	15	17	18	20	22	24	26	27	29	32	11:1
11:2	0	2	4	6	8	10	11	13	15	16	17	19	20	22	24	26	27	29	32	11:2
11:3	0	3	5	7	8	10	12	13	15	16	17	19	20	22	24	26	27	29	32	11:3
11:4	0	3	5	7	8	10	12	14	15	16	18	19	20	22	24	26	27	29	32	11:4
11:5	1	3	5	7	9	11	12	14	15	16	18	19	21	23	24	26	27	29	32	11:5
11:6	1	4	5	7	9	11	12	14	15	16	18	19	21	23	24	26	27	29	32	11:6
11:7	1	4	5	8	9	11	13	14	16	17	18	19	21	23	24	26	27	29	32	11:7
11:8	2	4	6	8	10	11	13	15	16	17	18	20	21	23	25	26	27	29	32	11:8
11:9	2	5	6	8	10	12	13	15	16	17	19	20	21	23	25	26	27	29	32	11:9
11:10	2	5	7	9	10	12	13	15	16	17	19	20	21	23	25	27	28	29	33	11:10
11:11	3	5	7	9	10	12	14	15	16	17	19	20	22	23	25	27	28	29	33	11:11
12:0	3	5	7	9	11	12	14	15	17	18	19	20	22	23	25	27	28	29	33	12:0
12:1	3	6	7	9	11	13	14	16	17	18	19	20	22	24	25	27	28	30	33	12:1
12:2	4	6	8	10	11	13	14	16	17	18	19	21	22	24	25	27	28	30	33	12:2
12:3	4	6	8	10	13	13	15	16	17	18	20	21	22	24	25	27	28	30	33	12:3
12:4	4	7	8	10	12	13	15	16	17	18	20	21	22	24	26	27	28	30	33	12:4
12:5	5	7	9	11	12	14	15	17	18	19	20	21	22	24	26	27	28	30	33	12:5
12:6	5	7	9	11	12	14	15	17	18	19	20	21	23	24	26	27	28	30	33	12:6
12:7	5	7	9	11	12	14	15	17	18	19	20	21	23	24	26	27	28	30	33	12:7
12:8	5	8	9	11	13	15	16	17	18	19	21	22	23	25	26	27	28	30	33	12:8
12:9	5	8	10	12	13	15	16	18	19	19	21	22	23	25	26	28	28	30	33	12:9
12:10	6	8	10	12	13	15	16	18	19	20	21	22	23	25	26	28	29	30	33	12:10
12:11	6	9	10	12	14	15	16	18	19	20	21	22	23	25	26	28	29	30	33	12:11
13:0	6	9	10	12	14	15	17	18	19	20	21	22	24	25	26	28	29	30	33	13:0
13:1	7	9	11	13	14	16	17	18	19	20	22	23	24	25	27	28	29	30	33	13:1
13:2	7	9	11	13	14	16	17	19	20	20	22	23	24	25	27	28	29	30	33	13:2
13:3	7	10	11	13	15	16	17	19	20	21	22	23	24	26	27	28	29	30	33	13:3
13:4	8	10	12	14	15	16	18	19	20	21	22	23	24	26	27	28	29	30	33	13:4
13:5	8	11	12	14	15	17	18	19	20	21	22	23	24	26	27	28	29	30	33	13:5
5%	5%	10%	15%	20%	25%	30%	35%	40%	45%	50%	55%	60%	65%	70%	75%	80%	85%	90%	95%	95%
										Percentile										

Age	5%	10%	15%	20%	25%	30%	35%	40%	45%	50%	55%	60%	65%	70%	75%	80%	85%	90%	95%	Age
13:6	9	11	12	14	15	17	18	20	20	21	22	23	25	26	27	28	29	31	33	13:6
13:7	9	11	13	14	16	17	18	20	21	21	23	24	25	26	27	29	29	31	33	13:7
13:8	9	11	13	15	16	17	19	20	21	22	23	24	25	26	27	29	29	31	33	13:8
13:9	10	12	13	15	16	18	19	20	21	22	23	24	25	26	28	29	30	31	33	13:9
13:10	10	12	14	15	17	18	19	20	21	22	23	24	25	27	28	29	30	31	33	13:10
13:11	10	12	14	16	17	18	19	21	22	22	24	24	25	27	28	29	30	31	33	13:11
14:0	11	13	14	16	17	18	20	21	22	23	24	25	26	27	28	29	30	31	33	14:0
14:1	11	13	14	16	17	19	20	21	22	23	24	25	26	27	28	29	30	31	33	14:1
14:2	11	13	15	16	18	19	20	21	22	23	24	25	26	27	28	29	30	31	33	14:2
14:3	11	14	15	17	18	19	20	22	23	23	24	25	26	27	28	29	30	31	33	14:3
14:4	12	14	15	17	18	19	21	22	23	24	25	25	26	27	28	29	30	31	33	14:4
14:5	12	14	16	17	18	20	21	22	23	24	25	26	26	28	29	29	30	31	33	14:5
14:6	12	15	16	17	19	20	21	22	23	24	25	26	27	28	29	30	30	31	33	14:6
14:7	13	15	16	18	19	20	21	23	23	24	25	26	27	28	29	30	30	31	33	14:7
14:8	13	15	17	18	19	20	22	23	23	24	25	26	27	28	29	30	30	31	33	14:8
14:9	13	15	17	18	19	21	22	23	24	25	26	26	27	28	29	30	31	31	33	14:9
14:10	14	16	17	19	20	21	22	23	24	25	26	26	27	28	29	30	31	32	33	14:10
14:11	14	16	17	19	20	21	22	24	24	25	26	27	28	28	29	30	31	32	33	14:11
15:0	14	16	18	19	20	21	23	24	25	25	26	27	28	29	29	30	31	32	33	15:0
15:1	15	17	18	19	20	22	23	24	25	25	26	27	28	29	29	30	31	32	33	15:1
15:2	15	17	18	20	21	22	23	24	25	26	26	27	28	29	30	30	31	32	33	15:2
15:3	15	17	19	20	21	22	23	25	25	26	26	27	28	29	30	30	31	32	33	15:3
15:4	16	18	19	20	21	22	23	25	25	26	27	27	28	29	30	31	31	32	33	15:4
15:5	16	18	19	21	22	23	24	25	26	26	27	28	28	29	30	31	31	32	33	15:5
15:6	16	18	19	21	22	23	24	26	26	26	27	28	29	29	30	31	31	32	33	15:6
15:7	16	18	19	21	22	23	24	26	26	27	27	28	29	29	30	31	31	32	33	15:7
15:8	17	19	20	21	23	24	25	26	26	27	28	28	29	30	30	31	31	32	33	15:8
15:9	17	19	20	22	23	24	25	26	26	27	28	28	29	30	31	31	32	32	33	15:9
15:10	17	19	20	22	23	24	25	26	26	27	28	29	29	30	31	31	32	32	33	15:10
15:11	18	20	21	22	23	24	25	26	27	27	28	29	29	30	31	31	32	32	33	15:11
5%		**10%**	**15%**	**20%**	**25%**	**30%**	**35%**	**40%**	**45%**	**50%**	**55%**	**60%**	**65%**	**70%**	**75%**	**80%**	**85%**	**90%**	**95%**	

Percentile

Test 4

Test 4

Diagnostic Spelling Test 4: Standardised scores

Raw score	Age in years and completed months																											Raw score
	13:2	13:1	13:0	12:11	12:10	12:9	12:8	12:7	12:6	12:5	12:4	12:3	12:2	12:1	12:0	11:11	11:10	11:9	11:8	11:7	11:6	11:5	11:4	11:3	11:2	11:1	11:0	
1												70-	70-	70-	70-	70-	70-	70-	71	73	74	76	77	77	78	78	79	1
2											70-	70-	70-	70-	71	72	73	75	76	77	78	78	79	79	80	80	81	2
3							70-	70-	70-	70-	70-	71	72	74	76	77	77	78	78	79	79	80	80	81	81	82	83	3
4			70-	70-	70-	70-	74	74	77	77	75	76	77	77	78	78	79	79	80	81	81	82	82	83	84	84	85	4
5	70-	70-	73	74	76	72	77	77	79	79	78	78	79	79	80	80	81	81	82	83	83	84	84	85	85	86	86	5
6	71	71	77	78	78	77	79	79	81	81	80	80	81	81	82	82	83	84	84	85	85	86	86	86	87	87	88	6
7	75	77	79	80	80	79	81	81	83	83	82	82	83	83	84	84	85	85	86	86	87	87	87	88	88	88	89	7
8	78	78	81	82	82	81	83	83	85	85	84	84	85	85	86	86	87	87	87	87	88	88	89	89	90	89	90	8
9	80	80	83	84	84	83	85	85	87	86	86	86	86	87	87	87	88	88	89	89	89	90	90	91	91	91	92	9
10	82	82	85	86	86	85	87	87	88	88	87	87	88	88	89	88	89	90	90	91	91	91	92	92	92	93	93	10
11	84	84	87	88	88	87	88	89	89	89	89	89	89	90	90	89	91	91	92	92	92	93	93	93	94	94	94	11
12	86	86	88	89	89	88	90	90	91	91	90	90	91	91	92	91	92	93	93	93	94	94	94	95	95	95	96	12
13	88	88	90	91	91	90	92	92	92	92	92	92	92	93	93	92	94	94	94	95	95	95	96	96	96	97	97	13
14	89	90	92	92	92	91	93	93	94	94	93	93	94	94	94	93	95	96	96	96	97	97	97	98	98	98	99	14
15	91	91	93	94	94	93	95	95	95	95	95	95	95	96	96	95	97	97	97	98	98	98	99	99	99	100	100	15
16	92	93	95	95	95	94	96	96	97	96	96	96	96	97	98	96	98	99	99	99	100	100	100	101	101	101	101	16
17	94	94	96	97	97	96	98	98	98	98	98	98	98	99	99	98	100	100	100	101	101	101	102	101	102	102	103	17
18	96	96	98	99	99	98	100	100	100	100	99	100	100	100	101	100	101	102	102	102	102	103	103	103	103	104	104	18
19	97	98	100	100	101	100	101	101	101	101	101	101	101	102	102	101	103	103	103	104	104	104	104	105	105	105	105	19
20	99	100	102	102	102	101	103	103	102	103	102	103	103	103	104	102	104	104	105	105	105	105	106	106	106	106	107	20
21	101	101	103	104	104	103	104	104	104	104	104	104	104	105	105	104	106	106	106	106	107	107	107	107	107	108	108	21
22	103	103	105	105	106	104	106	106	105	106	106	106	106	106	107	105	107	107	107	108	108	108	108	108	109	109	109	22
23	104	105	107	107	107	106	108	108	107	107	107	107	107	108	108	107	108	109	109	109	109	109	110	110	110	110	110	23
24	106	106	108	109	109	107	109	109	108	109	108	109	109	109	109	108	110	110	110	110	111	111	111	111	111	112	112	24
25	108	108	110	111	111	109	111	111	110	110	110	110	110	111	111	110	111	112	112	112	113	113	112	113	113	113	113	25
26	109	110	112	113	113	111	113	113	112	112	112	112	112	112	113	111	113	113	113	114	114	114	114	114	115	115	115	26
27	111	112	114	115	115	113	115	115	114	114	114	114	114	114	114	113	115	115	115	115	116	116	116	116	116	116	117	27
28	113	114	116	117	117	115	117	117	116	116	116	116	116	116	116	115	117	117	117	117	117	117	118	118	118	118	118	28
29	116	116	118	119	119	117	119	119	118	118	118	118	118	118	118	117	119	119	119	119	119	119	119	120	120	120	120	29
30	118	118	120	121	121	119	121	121	120	120	120	120	120	120	120	118	120	121	121	121	121	120	120	120	121	121	121	30
31	120	120	121	123	123	121	123	121	122	122	122	122	122	122	122	120	122	122	122	122	122	121	121	121	122	123	123	31
32	122	122	122	127	127	127	127	122	126	127	123	123	123	123	123	122	123	124	124	124	124	124	124	125	125	125	125	32
33	126	126	126	128	128	128	128	128	128	128	128	128	128	128	128	128	128	128	128	129	129	129	129	129	129	129	129	33
34	130+	130+	130+	130+	130+	130+	130+	130+	130+	130+	130+	130+	130+	130+	130+	130+	130+	130+	130+	130+	130+	130+	130+	130+	130+	130+	130+	34
35																												35
36																												36
37																												37
38																												38
39																												39
40																												40
	13:2	13:1	13:0	12:11	12:10	12:9	12:8	12:7	12:6	12:5	12:4	12:3	12:2	12:1	12:0	11:11	11:10	11:9	11:8	11:7	11:6	11:5	11:4	11:3	11:2	11:1	11:0	
Raw score	Age in years and completed months																											Raw score

Age in years and completed months

Raw score	13:3	13:4	13:5	13:6	13:7	13:8	13:9	13:10	13:11	14:0	14:1	14:2	14:3	14:4	14:5	14:6	14:7	14:8	14:9	14:10	14:11	15:0	15:1	15:2	15:3	15:4	15:5	Raw score
1																												1
2																												2
3																												3
4																												4
5																												5
6	70-																											6
7	73	70-	70-																									7
8	77	72	76	70-	70-	70-																						8
9	79	77	78	74	72	71	70-	70-	70-																			9
10	81	79	80	78	77	76	77	73	71	70-	70-	70-	70-															10
11	83	81	82	82	79	78	79	77	77	75	74	72	76	70-	70-	70-												11
12	86	83	84	84	81	80	81	79	79	78	77	77	78	74	73	71	70-	70-		70-	70-	70-	70-					12
13	87	85	86	86	83	83	84	81	81	80	79	79	80	78	77	77	75	73	70-	76	74	72	71	70-	70-	70-		13
14	89	87	88	87	85	85	86	84	83	82	82	81	83	80	79	79	78	77	72	78	78	77	76	75	73	71	70-	14
15	90	88	89	89	87	87	88	86	85	85	84	83	85	82	81	81	80	79	77	80	80	79	78	78	77	77	75	15
16	92	90	91	91	89	88	89	87	87	86	86	85	87	84	84	83	82	82	79	83	82	81	81	80	79	79	78	16
17	94	92	92	92	90	90	91	89	89	88	88	87	88	86	86	85	85	84	81	85	84	84	83	82	82	81	80	17
18	95	93	94	94	92	91	93	91	90	90	89	89	90	88	87	87	87	86	83	87	86	86	85	85	84	83	83	18
19	97	95	96	96	94	93	94	92	92	91	91	91	92	90	89	89	88	88	86	89	88	88	87	87	86	86	85	19
20	99	97	98	98	95	95	96	94	94	93	93	92	94	93	91	92	90	90	88	90	90	89	89	89	88	88	87	20
21	101	99	100	99	97	97	98	96	96	95	95	94	96	95	93	94	92	91	90	92	92	91	91	90	90	89	89	21
22	102	101	101	101	99	99	100	98	98	97	96	96	98	97	95	96	94	93	92	94	94	93	93	92	92	91	91	22
23	104	102	103	103	101	101	102	100	99	99	98	98	100	99	97	98	96	95	94	96	96	95	95	94	94	93	93	23
24	106	104	105	105	103	102	104	102	101	101	100	100	102	101	99	100	98	97	96	99	98	98	97	97	96	95	95	24
25	107	105	106	107	105	104	106	104	103	103	102	102	104	103	101	102	100	99	98	101	100	100	99	99	98	98	97	25
26	109	107	108	108	106	106	108	105	105	105	104	104	106	105	103	105	102	102	100	103	103	102	102	101	101	100	100	26
27	111	109	110	110	108	108	109	107	107	107	106	106	108	107	105	107	104	104	102	105	105	104	104	104	103	103	102	27
28	113	111	112	112	110	110	112	109	109	109	108	108	110	109	107	109	106	106	104	107	107	107	106	106	106	105	105	28
29	115	113	114	115	112	112	114	111	111	111	110	110	112	112	109	111	108	108	106	110	109	109	109	108	108	108	107	29
30	118	115	117	117	114	114	116	114	113	113	113	112	115	114	111	114	111	110	108	113	112	112	111	111	111	110	110	30
31	120	118	119	120	117	117	119	116	116	116	115	115	118	118	114	117	114	113	111	116	115	115	115	114	114	114	113	31
32	122	120	122	122	120	119	121	119	119	119	118	118	121	121	117	120	117	116	116	119	119	119	118	118	118	117	117	32
33	126	125	124	125	122	122	124	121	121	124	123	123	123	123	123	123	120	123	120	122	122	122	122	122	122	121	121	33
34	130+	130+	130+	130+	130+	130+	130+	130+	130+	130+	130+	130+	130+	130+	130+	130+	130+	130+	130	130	130	129	129	129	129	128	128	34
35																			130+	130+	130+	130+	130+	130+	130+	130+	130+	35
36																												36
37																												37
38																												38
39																												39
40																												40
Raw score	13:3	13:4	13:5	13:6	13:7	13:8	13:9	13:10	13:11	14:0	14:1	14:2	14:3	14:4	14:5	14:6	14:7	14:8	14:9	14:10	14:11	15:0	15:1	15:2	15:3	15:4	15:5	Raw score

Age in years and completed months

Diagnostic Spelling Test 4: Item facilities, by Year group

FORM A	Year 7	Year 8	Year 9	Year 10	Year 11	Overall	FORM B	Year 7	Year 8	Year 9	Year 10	Year 11	Overall
audible	.17	.19	.31	.23	.55	.23	fierce	.51	.57	.56	.55	.45	.55
straight	.77	.76	.88	.84	.91	.81	outrageous	.27	.34	.39	.32	.50	.34
Wednesday	.91	.93	.92	.94	1	.92	February	.38	.48	.44	.48	.45	.44
development	.79	.82	.88	.90	1	.85	permanent	.22	.32	.26	.20	.50	.27
design	.69	.77	.86	.89	1	.79	columns	.24	.22	.28	.32	.41	.26
necessary	.23	.25	.27	.28	.50	.26	disappoint	.15	.12	.16	.13	.27	.15
fulfil	.1	.10	.09	.11	.50	.11	skilful	.16	.06	.14	.07	.09	.11
beautiful	.66	.71	.78	.84	.86	.74	daughter	.78	.88	.89	.90	1	.86
unfortunately	.27	.24	.29	.27	.50	.27	sincerely	.37	.23	.28	.20	.45	.29
separate	.33	.30	.23	.31	.36	.29	definite	.19	.17	.14	.12	.14	.16
allowed	.64	.65	.68	.82	.77	.68	braking	.37	.38	.42	.31	.41	.38
course	.73	.78	.75	.89	.77	.77	practice	.51	.62	.66	.66	.59	.61
frieze	.06	.06	.08	.09	.14	.07	portrait	.56	.66	.66	.66	.77	.64
exhibition	.30	.36	.41	.43	.77	.38	illusion	.44	.56	.68	.67	.91	.58
hygiene	.24	.21	.28	.39	.27	.26	protein	.45	.56	.63	.67	.86	.57
recipe	.45	.56	.60	.51	.64	.54	portfolio	.44	.48	.70	.62	.73	.56
theatre	.51	.68	.59	.68	.77	.61	rehearse	.44	.47	.39	.55	.36	.44
applause	.57	.53	.55	.66	.73	.57	dramatise	.64	.67	.69	.72	.73	.68
dialogue	.23	.37	.36	.46	.82	.35	grammar	.36	.42	.42	.37	.36	.39
atmosphere	.60	.69	.74	.86	1	.71	pamphlet	.10	.10	.14	.16	.27	.12
country	.88	.89	.92	.96	.95	.91	tourism	.44	.68	.73	.82	.91	.66
region	.64	.66	.75	.82	.86	.70	erosion	.34	.59	.58	.50	.73	.52
disease	.38	.50	.52	.68	.73	.50	traitor	.28	.45	.51	.51	.73	.44
parliament	.13	.17	.36	.19	.36	.22	agriculture	.32	.47	.53	.56	.91	.47
cursor	.35	.35	.41	.33	.59	.37	memory	.69	.83	.85	.89	.95	.81
module	.50	.66	.75	.85	.91	.67	document	.75	.89	.90	.92	.82	.86
dictionary	.72	.75	.80	.91	.91	.78	glossary	.60	.69	.74	.78	.77	.69
catalogue	.23	.38	.38	.48	.55	.36	copyright	.57	.75	.77	.82	.77	.72
parallel	.24	.26	.35	.32	.55	.30	symmetrical	.12	.09	.16	.09	.05	.12
circumference	.26	.33	.35	.50	.59	.34	percentage	.64	.80	.88	.94	.95	.80
orchestra	.27	.62	.50	.43	.64	.47	choir	.49	.55	.52	.66	.86	.55
rhythm	.16	.19	.22	.27	.73	.21	musician	.47	.50	.53	.56	.91	.52
mobility	.65	.74	.80	.81	.95	.75	activity	.67	.73	.85	.89	.86	.77
league	.43	.57	.66	.70	.91	.59	medicine	.47	.57	.57	.56	.77	.55
generosity	.24	.44	.45	.44	.73	.40	dependency	.40	.33	.35	.49	.55	.38
approval	.43	.57	.62	.64	.77	.56	ability	.67	.73	.81	.88	.91	.76
commitment	.37	.53	.60	.67	.68	.53	celebration	.61	.69	.76	.80	.91	.71
religious	.32	.41	.50	.57	.77	.44	prejudice	.09	.15	.20	.13	.45	.15
laboratory	.21	.27	.32	.35	.64	.29	temperature	.44	.58	.59	.57	.91	.56
amphibian	.33	.51	.41	.44	.59	.43	frequency	.47	.65	.67	.84	1	.64
Average facility	**.42**	**.49**	**.53**	**.57**	**.71**	**.50**	Average facility	**.43**	**.50**	**.54**	**.55**	**.65**	**.50**

85

Test 4

Diagnostic Spelling Test 5: Percentiles

Age	5%	10%	15%	20%	25%	30%	35%	40%	45%	50%	55%	60%	65%	70%	75%	80%	85%	90%	95%	Age
14:0	17	19	21	23	24	25	26	27	27	28	29	30	31	31	32	33	34	35	37	14:0
14:1	17	20	21	23	24	25	26	27	27	28	29	30	31	31	32	33	34	35	37	14:1
14:2	17	20	21	23	24	25	26	27	28	28	29	30	31	31	32	33	34	35	37	14:2
14:3	17	20	21	23	24	25	26	27	28	28	29	30	31	32	32	33	34	35	37	14:3
14:4	17	20	21	23	24	25	26	27	28	29	29	30	31	32	32	33	35	36	37	14:4
14:5	17	20	21	23	24	25	26	27	28	29	29	30	31	32	32	33	35	36	37	14:5
14:6	17	20	21	23	24	25	26	27	28	29	29	30	31	32	33	34	35	36	37	14:6
14:7	17	20	21	23	24	25	26	27	28	29	30	30	31	32	33	34	35	36	37	14:7
14:8	17	20	21	23	25	26	26	27	28	29	30	31	31	32	33	34	35	36	37	14:8
14:9	17	20	21	23	25	26	26	27	28	29	30	31	31	32	33	34	35	36	37	14:9
14:10	17	20	21	23	25	26	27	27	28	29	30	31	31	32	33	34	35	36	37	14:10
14:11	17	20	21	23	25	26	27	28	28	29	30	31	31	32	33	34	35	36	37	14:11
15:0	17	20	21	24	25	26	27	28	28	29	30	31	32	32	33	34	35	36	37	15:0
15:1	17	20	22	24	25	26	27	28	29	29	30	31	32	32	33	34	35	36	37	15:1
15:2	16	20	22	24	26	26	27	28	29	29	30	31	32	32	33	34	35	36	37	15:2
15:3	16	20	22	24	26	26	27	28	29	30	30	31	32	33	33	34	36	36	37	15:3
15:4	16	20	22	24	25	26	27	28	29	30	30	31	32	33	33	34	35	36	38	15:4
15:5	16	20	22	24	25	26	27	28	29	30	30	31	32	33	33	34	35	36	38	15:5
15:6	16	20	22	24	25	26	27	28	29	30	31	31	32	33	34	34	35	36	38	15:6
15:7	16	20	22	24	25	27	27	28	29	30	31	31	32	33	34	35	36	36	38	15:7
15:8	16	20	22	24	26	27	28	28	29	30	31	32	32	33	34	35	36	36	38	15:8
15:9	16	20	22	24	26	27	28	28	29	30	31	32	32	33	34	35	36	37	38	15:9
15:10	16	20	22	24	26	27	28	29	29	30	31	32	32	33	34	35	36	37	38	15:10
15:11	16	20	22	24	26	27	28	29	30	30	31	32	33	33	34	35	36	37	38	15:11
	5%	10%	15%	20%	25%	30%	35%	40%	45%	50%	55%	60%	65%	70%	75%	80%	85%	90%	95%	

Percentile

Age	5%	10%	15%	20%	25%	30%	35%	40%	45%	50%	55%	60%	65%	70%	75%	80%	85%	90%	95%	Age
16:0	16	20	22	24	26	27	28	29	30	30	31	32	33	33	34	35	36	37	38	16:0
16:1	16	21	22	25	26	27	28	29	30	30	31	32	33	33	34	35	36	37	38	16:1
16:2	16	21	22	25	26	27	28	29	30	31	31	32	33	34	34	35	36	37	38	16:2
16:3	16	21	22	25	26	27	28	29	30	31	31	32	33	34	34	35	36	37	38	16:3
16:4	16	21	22	25	26	27	28	29	30	31	31	32	33	34	34	35	36	37	38	16:4
16:5	16	21	22	25	26	27	28	29	30	31	32	32	33	34	34	35	36	37	38	16:5
16:6	16	21	23	25	26	28	28	29	30	31	32	32	33	34	34	35	36	37	38	16:6
16:7	16	21	23	25	27	28	29	29	30	31	32	33	33	34	35	35	36	37	38	16:7
16:8	16	21	23	25	27	28	29	29	30	31	32	33	33	34	35	35	36	37	38	16:8
16:9	16	21	23	25	27	28	29	30	30	31	32	33	33	34	35	35	36	37	38	16:9
16:10	16	21	23	25	27	28	29	30	31	31	32	33	33	34	35	36	37	37	38	16:10
16:11	16	21	23	25	27	28	29	30	31	31	32	33	34	34	35	36	37	37	38	16:11
17:0	16	21	23	25	27	28	29	30	31	32	32	33	34	34	35	36	37	37	38	17:0
17:1	16	21	23	25	27	28	29	30	31	32	32	33	34	34	35	36	37	37	38	17:1
17:2	16	21	23	26	27	28	29	30	31	32	32	33	34	35	35	36	37	38	39	17:2
17:3	16	21	23	26	27	28	29	30	31	32	32	33	34	35	35	36	37	38	39	17:3
17:4	16	21	23	26	27	28	29	30	31	32	33	33	34	35	35	36	37	38	39	17:4
17:5	16	21	23	26	27	29	29	30	31	32	33	33	34	35	35	36	37	38	39	17:5
17:6	16	21	23	26	28	29	30	30	31	32	33	34	34	35	36	36	37	38	39	17:6
17:7	16	21	23	26	28	29	30	31	31	32	33	34	34	35	36	36	37	38	39	17:7
17:8	16	21	23	26	28	29	30	31	31	32	33	34	34	35	36	36	37	38	39	17:8
17:9	16	21	23	26	28	29	30	31	32	32	33	34	34	35	36	36	37	38	39	17:9
17:10	16	21	23	26	28	29	30	31	32	32	33	34	35	35	36	37	37	38	39	17:10
17:11	16	21	24	26	28	29	30	31	32	33	33	34	35	35	36	37	37	38	39	17:11
	5%	10%	15%	20%	25%	30%	35%	40%	45%	50%	55%	60%	65%	70%	75%	80%	85%	90%	95%	

Percentile

Test 5

Test 5

Diagnostic Spelling Test 5: Standardised scores

Age in years and completed months

Raw score	14:0	14:1	14:2	14:3	14:4	14:5	14:6	14:7	14:8	14:9	14:10	14:11	15:0	15:1	15:2	15:3	15:4	15:5	15:6	15:7	15:8	15:9	15:10	15:11	Raw score
1																									1
2																									2
3																									3
4																									4
5																									5
6																									6
7																									7
8																									8
9																									9
10																									10
11																									11
12																									12
13																									13
14	70-	70-	70-	70-	70-	70-	70-	70-	70-	70-	70-	70-	70-	70-	70-	70-	70-	70-	70-	70-	70-	70-	70-	70-	14
15	70	70	70	71	71	71	71	71	71	71	71	72	70-	70-	70-	70-	70-	70-	70-	70-	70-	70-	70-	70-	15
16	74	74	74	74	74	74	74	74	75	75	75	75	72	72	72	72	72	72	72	72	72	72	72	72	16
17	77	77	77	77	77	77	77	77	77	77	77	77	75	75	75	75	75	75	75	75	75	75	75	75	17
18	80	80	79	79	79	79	79	79	79	79	79	79	77	77	77	77	77	77	77	77	77	77	77	77	18
19	82	82	82	82	82	82	82	81	81	81	81	81	79	79	79	79	79	79	79	79	79	78	78	78	19
20	85	85	85	85	84	84	84	84	84	84	84	84	81	81	81	81	81	80	80	80	80	80	80	80	20
21	87	87	87	86	86	86	86	86	86	86	86	86	83	83	83	83	83	83	83	83	82	82	82	82	21
22	88	88	88	88	88	88	88	87	87	87	87	87	85	85	85	85	85	85	85	85	85	85	84	84	22
23	90	90	90	89	89	89	89	89	89	89	89	88	87	87	87	87	87	86	86	86	86	86	86	86	23
24	92	92	92	92	91	91	91	91	90	90	90	90	88	88	88	88	88	88	88	88	88	87	87	87	24
25	95	95	94	94	94	94	94	93	93	93	93	92	90	90	90	89	89	89	89	89	89	89	89	89	25
26	97	97	97	97	96	96	96	96	96	95	95	95	92	92	92	91	91	91	91	91	90	90	90	90	26
27	100	99	99	99	99	99	98	98	98	98	97	97	95	94	94	94	94	94	93	93	93	93	92	92	27
28	102	102	102	101	101	101	101	100	100	100	100	100	97	97	97	96	96	96	96	96	95	95	95	95	28
29	104	104	104	104	104	103	103	103	103	102	102	102	99	99	99	99	98	98	98	98	98	97	97	97	29
30	107	107	107	106	106	106	106	105	105	105	105	105	102	102	101	101	101	101	100	100	100	100	100	99	30
31	110	110	110	109	109	109	109	108	108	108	108	107	104	104	104	104	103	103	103	103	102	102	102	102	31
32	112	112	112	112	111	111	111	111	111	111	110	110	107	107	107	106	106	106	106	105	105	105	105	104	32
33	115	114	114	114	114	114	114	113	113	113	113	113	110	110	110	109	109	109	109	108	108	108	108	107	33
34	118	118	118	117	117	117	117	116	116	116	116	115	113	112	112	112	112	112	111	111	111	111	111	110	34
35	122	121	121	121	121	121	121	120	120	120	120	119	115	115	115	115	114	114	114	114	114	113	113	113	35
36	128	127	127	127	126	126	125	125	124	124	123	123	119	119	119	118	118	118	118	117	117	117	117	116	36
37	130+	130+	130+	130+	130+	130+	130+	130+	130+	130+	130+	130+	123	123	123	122	122	122	122	122	121	121	121	121	37
38													130+	130+	130+	130+	130+	130+	130	129	129	128	128	127	38
39																				130+..	130+..	130+..	130+..	130+..	39
40																									40
Raw score	14:0	14:1	14:2	14:3	14:4	14:5	14:6	14:7	14:8	14:9	14:10	14:11	15:0	15:1	15:2	15:3	15:4	15:5	15:6	15:7	15:8	15:9	15:10	15:11	Raw score

Age in years and completed months

Test 5

Raw score	16:0	16:1	16:2	16:3	16:4	16:5	16:6	16:7	16:8	16:9	16:10	16:11	17:00	17:01	17:2	17:3	17:4	17:5	17:6	17:7	17:8	17:9	17:10	17:11
1																								
2																								
3																								
4																								
5																								
6																								
7																								
8																								
9																								
10																								
11																								
12																								
13																								
14		70-	70-	70-	70-	70-	70-	70-	70-	70-	70-	70-	70-	70-	70-	70-	70-	70-	70-	70-	70-	70-	70-	70-
15	70-	70	70	70	70	70	71	71	71	71	71	71	71	71	71	71	71	71	71	71	71	71	71	71
16	72	72	72	73	73	73	73	73	73	73	73	73	73	73	73	73	73	73	73	73	73	73	73	73
17	75	75	75	75	75	75	75	75	75	75	75	75	75	75	75	75	75	75	75	75	75	75	75	75
18	77	77	77	77	77	77	77	77	77	77	77	77	77	77	77	77	77	77	77	77	77	77	77	77
19	78	78	78	78	78	78	78	78	78	78	78	78	78	78	78	78	78	78	78	78	78	78	78	78
20	80	80	80	80	80	80	80	80	79	79	79	79	79	79	79	79	79	79	79	79	79	79	79	79
21	82	82	82	82	82	81	81	81	81	81	81	81	81	81	81	81	81	80	80	80	80	80	80	80
22	84	84	84	84	84	84	83	83	83	83	83	83	83	83	83	83	82	82	82	82	82	82	82	82
23	86	86	86	86	86	85	85	85	85	85	85	85	85	85	85	84	84	84	84	84	84	84	84	84
24	87	87	87	87	87	87	87	87	86	86	86	86	86	86	86	86	86	86	86	86	85	85	85	85
25	88	88	88	88	88	88	88	88	88	88	87	87	87	87	87	87	87	87	87	87	87	87	86	86
26	90	90	90	89	89	89	89	89	89	89	89	89	89	88	88	88	88	88	88	88	88	88	88	88
27	92	92	92	91	91	91	91	91	90	90	90	90	90	90	90	89	89	89	89	89	89	89	89	89
28	94	94	94	94	94	93	93	93	93	92	92	92	92	92	91	91	91	91	91	90	90	90	90	90
29	97	97	96	96	96	96	96	95	95	95	95	94	94	94	94	94	93	93	93	93	93	92	92	92
30	99	99	99	98	98	98	98	98	97	97	97	97	97	96	96	96	96	96	95	95	95	95	94	94
31	102	101	101	101	101	100	100	100	100	99	99	99	99	99	98	98	100	98	98	97	97	97	97	97
32	104	104	104	103	103	103	103	103	102	102	102	102	101	101	101	101	100	100	100	100	99	99	99	99
33	107	107	107	106	106	106	105	105	105	105	104	104	104	104	104	103	103	103	103	102	102	102	102	101
34	110	110	110	109	109	109	109	108	108	108	108	107	107	107	106	106	106	106	105	105	105	105	104	104
35	113	113	112	112	112	112	112	111	111	111	111	111	110	110	110	110	109	109	109	108	108	108	108	107
36	116	116	115	115	115	115	114	114	114	114	114	113	113	113	113	113	112	112	112	112	111	111	111	111
37	120	120	120	120	119	119	119	119	118	118	118	117	117	117	116	116	116	115	115	115	115	114	114	114
38	127	126	126	125	125	124	123	123	123	123	123	122	122	122	121	121	121	121	120	120	120	119	119	119
39	130+	130+	130+	130+	130+	130+	130+	130+	130+	130+	130+	130+	130+	130+	130+	130+	130+	130	129	129	128	127	127	126
40	130+	130+	130+	130+	130+	130+	130+	130+	130+	130+	130+	130+	130+	130+	130+	130+	130+	130+	130+	130+	130+	130+	130+	130+

Age in years and completed months

Diagnostic Spelling Test 5: Item facilities, by Year group

FORM A	Year 10	Year 11	Year 12	Year 13	Trainees	Overall	FORM B	Year 10	Year 11	Year 12	Year 13	Trainees	Overall
disappear	.65	.57	.82	.75	.36	.67	embarrass	.16	.13	.17	.16	.19	.16
believe	.88	.91	.97	.96	.88	.92	relief	.86	.90	.94	.94	.78	.90
assessment	.57	.51	.73	.75	.68	.64	accommodation	.14	.19	.18	.28	.17	.19
argument	.70	.71	.68	.77	.60	.70	continuous	.71	.69	.88	.92	.64	.78
knowledge	.88	.92	.98	.98	.86	.93	guard	.91	.89	.94	.97	.87	.92
potential	.91	.92	.97	.97	.88	.94	industrial	.94	.93	.98	.96	.96	.95
participation	.84	.87	.95	.94	.76	.89	persuasion	.48	.50	.65	.55	.35	.53
unnecessary	.44	.46	.61	.63	.31	.51	occurred	.39	.33	.51	.46	.36	.41
grateful	.67	.66	.72	.75	.50	.68	successful	.65	.66	.85	.82	.56	.72
naturally	.84	.84	.92	.97	.81	.88	practically	.69	.77	.90	.93	.68	.81
persistent	.42	.31	.42	.44	.42	.40	independent	.35	.29	.38	.54	.32	.37
effect	.94	.98	.99	.99	.91	.97	affected	.85	.88	.96	.96	.77	.90
environment	.80	.74	.93	.92	.72	.83	government	.88	.89	.98	.99	.72	.91
permanent	.60	.60	.73	.73	.42	.64	behaviour	.86	.86	.95	.92	.71	.88
truancy	.50	.58	.72	.67	.38	.59	university	.89	.90	.94	.96	.82	.91
optician	.69	.65	.84	.88	.60	.75	electrician	.71	.75	.92	.91	.79	.82
accepted	.90	.92	.98	.99	.88	.94	dissipated	.26	.31	.44	.43	.19	.34
career	.76	.82	.89	.92	.68	.83	weird	.68	.66	.65	.65	.76	.67
simultaneous	.54	.59	.77	.77	.33	.63	tremendously	.69	.73	.90	.93	.56	.78
excess	.88	.93	.96	.98	.71	.91	except	.83	.84	.95	.94	.64	.87
exaggerate	.44	.49	.73	.73	.31	.56	immediate	.70	.71	.89	.92	.49	.77
request	.95	.98	.98	.96	.96	.97	queue	.62	.69	.74	.87	.44	.70
glamorous	.41	.44	.48	.41	.38	.43	gorgeous	.20	.20	.38	.31	.42	.29
achieve	.81	.81	.89	.90	.77	.84	receive	.33	.36	.54	.55	.28	.43
gauge	.42	.49	.6	.61	.51	.52	mortgage	.71	.70	.84	.88	.62	.76
transferred	.63	.64	.86	.82	.60	.72	selected	.96	.96	1	.98	.94	.97
scent	.89	.88	.93	.96	.72	.90	whether	.68	.84	.91	.89	.56	.80
extremely	.66	.66	.84	.83	.62	.73	library	.87	.89	.93	.93	.68	.88
privileged	.10	.08	.18	.18	.05	.13	college	.84	.91	.91	.96	.77	.89
certified	.87	.88	.93	.96	.76	.89	licence	.28	.31	.35	.36	.33	.32
occasion	.70	.77	.83	.79	.62	.76	decision	.70	.79	.90	.91	.67	.80
criticism	.54	.60	.81	.92	.51	.69	enthusiasm	.79	.88	.93	.95	.68	.86
paralysis	.48	.50	.63	.73	.32	.55	business	.77	.86	.91	.94	.76	.86
oscillate	.20	.18	.4	.38	.12	.27	exercises	.82	.82	.92	.94	.77	.86
supervisor	.83	.83	.95	.92	.76	.87	envisage	.69	.71	.86	.87	.71	.77
energetic	.91	.93	.98	.98	.83	.94	benefit	.78	.85	.90	.92	.71	.85
abundance	.72	.72	.83	.84	.51	.75	experience	.85	.87	.95	.93	.72	.88
similar	.92	.94	.96	.99	.73	.93	personal	.97	.98	.99	.99	.91	.97
alienated	.88	.93	.98	.96	.86	.93	limited	.97	.99	.96	.97	.99	.98
emptiness	.64	.66	.81	.79	.44	.70	variation	.91	.93	.99	.98	.82	.94
Average facility	**.69**	**.70**	**.80**	**.81**	**.60**	**.73**	**Average facility**	**.68**	**.71**	**.80**	**.81**	**.63**	**.74**

Diagnostic Spelling Test: Answer Sheet

First Name(s)		Last Name		Gender: Male / Female
Date of Birth	Date of Test	Class/Group		Test/Form taken
Raw score	Chronological age	Spelling age	Standardised score	Percentile

1		21	
2		22	
3		23	
4		24	
5		25	
6		26	
7		27	
8		28	
9		29	
10		30	
11		31	
12		32	
13		33	
14		34	
15		35	
16		36	
17		37	
18		38	
19		39	
20		40	